❧ THE BREAST LIFE™ GUIDE TO ❧

The
Bra Zone

How to Find
Your Ideal Size, Style,
and Support

Elisabeth Dale

Published by Mammoirs Media, Los Angeles, California
Copyright © 2016 Elisabeth Dale

Copyeditor: Lisa Canfield, www.copycoachlisa.com
Proofreader: Richard Feit, Richard Feit Editorial
Cover & interior design: Laura Shaw Design, Inc., lshawdesign.com
Cover & interior illustrations: Allison Meierding, allisonmeierding.com

Library of Congress Control Number: 2015902843
ISBN: 978-0-9903331-0-4

Quantity discounts are available on bulk purchases of this book for
educational or gift purposes, or as premiums for increasing magazine
subscriptions or renewals. Special books or book excerpts can also
be created to fit specific needs. For information, please contact
Mammoirs Media, info@thebreastlife.com.

Contents

Why the Bra Zone?

BACK IN THE LATE 60s, when I was 13 years old, my mom took me shopping for my first bra. She brought me to the intimate apparel section of the Bon Marché department store (now Macy's), where the old, intimidating saleswoman wasn't interested in my personal likes or dislikes. She looked me up and down and led me to the back wall. That's where they kept their stock of bras made for my 34D size—stiff, white, matronly cotton foundations more suited to a grandmother than a budding teenager.

The saleswoman ushered us into a dusty dressing room where she strapped me into an uncomfortable and unattractive constraint, then stood back and looked at me, proud of her accomplishment. My petite mother stared at me in the mirror and said by way of apology, "She got those from her father's side of the family."

The entire experience was embarrassing and depressing. I blamed my body for not being able to wear cute foundations. Even worse, I was stuck with bigger boobs when everyone else was celebrating wearing the latest braless fashions. My boobs would never draw a "Get Out of Bra Jail Free" card.

For most of my life, I've had a love/hate relationship with bra shopping. The frustrations of early puberty continued as my breasts kept on morphing. I went up and down the cup alphabet through weight fluctuations, three pregnancies, a cosmetic breast lift, and the hormonal mess known as menopause. Every time I thought I had my size figured out, everything changed again. And my boobs didn't just expand and contract, they also migrated. It's been tough trying to find bras that fit two moving targets on my chest.

Today, the journey that began with me uncomfortable with my size has come full circle. Since menopause, I'm back to wearing that original band-and-cup combo. However, almost everything else in the lingerie world has changed, including the bra industry.

I first noticed this in 2006, when I was researching my first book and helping my teen daughter navigate the complexities of bra shopping. The department store experience was still available, along with the hugely popular Victoria's Secret chain, but that was only the beginning. The online shopping world was expanding, making virtual bra shopping a reality.

But beyond that, for the first time, people were thinking about whether or not their bras fit properly, thanks to Oprah's famous "bra intervention" episode. Women realized that a well-fitting bra could change a person's life. These televised fittings marked the beginning of a new era in bra education, opening up conversations about fit that went beyond the A through D cups.

A decade later, today's bra world is filled with possibility. You'll find foundations everywhere: department stores, big box outlets, luxury boutiques, athletic shops, and, of course, online. If you don't have access to a professional bra fitter, you can use online surveys and phone apps to determine your bra size and style preferences. Some lingerie stores now video chat with customers to help them find their perfect foundations. You can search bra-wear reviews and match them to your size, body type, and age. Or you can follow any number of lingerie bloggers who test and share their recommendations.

There are lots to choose from—because the global lingerie market is bursting with more bra styles and sizes than ever before. You'll find cups from AAA to KK and beyond, depending on country of origin. There's more access to brands fitting a wider range of body shapes, with offerings spanning band size measurements from 26 to 58. New fabrics, elastics, and materials create an array of design options, from individual cut-and-sewn to machine-made molded cups. There's room for improvement regarding the diversity of offerings and models, but enterprising start-ups are working hard to fill any holes in the lucrative lingerie market.

As a result, we now have plenty of options beyond matronly white cotton, and that's a good thing. However, this bra-option overload can also be overwhelming. Finding a bra is still a challenge for me—and I'm not alone. Surveys show that women own an average of nine bras, yet only wear six on a regular basis. I get hundreds of questions from blog readers seeking solutions to their bra problems. Even those educated on bra sizing and fit have a hard time locating what they want.

Why is this happening?

It turns out that band and cup size is just a starting point. An ideal bra has to factor in your age, body shape, budget, fashion style, and more. Do you take yoga or run marathons? Want nipple coverage for work and a sexy plunging neckline for the evening? Are you just developing, or could you do with a new look post-baby? Maybe you're in the market for a nursing, mastectomy, or post-surgical bra. You may be a guy who either needs, or wants, to wear a bra.

In other words, there's more than size to consider.

The bad news is that the one thing you think you know—your size—is no longer relevant. Why? Brands have fit and sizing standards, but they're all different. You can't assume that identical letters and numbers on bra labels equal the same band length or breast cup volume. It's about more than knowing how to translate your size from one country to another, too. You need to understand the standard of measurement each manufacturer uses.

You've likely read that 85% of all women are in the wrong bra size. But there's no science behind that statistic. And I'm guessing the percentage is really 100%. Why? The reason women are in the "wrong size" has nothing to do with any ignorance about our bodies or bras. In truth, everyone wears more than one size across different brands and styles.

Which leaves the question, how can you navigate through all of the information out there and buy bras that work for you?

Welcome to *The Bra Zone*, where you will find the guidance you need to find your best bra, whether you're buying your first or your fiftieth.

Over the next few chapters, we'll unhook the mystery of bra fitting and sizing and let you decide what works best for your chest. We'll share tools to help you create your ideal "zone" of sizes and styles. You'll learn what a bra can—and can't—do for your figure, and about construction and bra shapes that suit specific fashion needs. You'll discover the vast range of possibilities in quality, price, and design, and where and how to shop for foundations. Plus, we'll cover washing and storage tips to help you extend the life of your lingerie investments, along with resources that cater to specific bra populations, so you can stay up to date and informed on your own changing Bra Zone.

Both the bra industry and the way women buy and wear bras have changed dramatically since my fateful trip to the Bon Marché. There's more to finding the right bra than one fixed size—there's a whole new world of fit, fashion, and function to explore. That's why I wrote this book: to empower you with the information you need to take charge of dressing your breasts. You can break the bra-shopping cycle of frustration and self-blame, and appreciate what a bra can (and can't) do for you. You'll find it easier to toss out old, ill-fitting bras, and discover bra bliss.

Are you ready to find the bras that fit and feel best on your body? Then follow me . . . into The Bra Zone.

CHAPTER 1

Breast Mysteries and Realities

WHAT'S TO KNOW about breasts? I never thought much about my own, except in comparison to others or the images I saw in magazines. It wasn't until my first pregnancy, when my boobs swelled up three times their "normal" size, that I realized the Herculean hormonal effort it took to turn them into mammary milk machines.

Up until that point, my breasts were simply another mystery of female puberty. They appeared on my chest when I didn't expect them. They never quite seemed to fit my body. Short of surgery, it was impossible to control their growth or change their size. They seemed to fluctuate in size every month. I could diet and not lose my boobs, or gain weight and have none of it go to my chest.

Or the exact opposite happened.

With all the attention breasts get in Western society, you'd think we'd know everything there is to know about them. So it's kind of a shock that there's so little actual breast data available. Research on average bra sizes, for instance, is conducted largely in secret by intimate apparel brands with the primary goal of increasing their consumer market share. So, of course, they don't release their findings to competitors, let alone provide the bra-wearing public with some much-needed clarity.

> Bra fitters claim that the average bra cup size has ballooned from C to E over the past twenty years.

And even if everyone got together and decided on one universal standard method of bust measurement, our ever-changing physical dimensions would still make relying on those measurements alone just about impossible.

We know that breasts are primarily made up of fat, glandular material, and thin strands of tissue that attach to the chest wall (called Cooper's ligaments). We also know that they exist to feed our babies and sustain human life. But after that, things start to get murky. For example, scientists have yet to reach a consensus on why women have these extra blobs of fat on their chests, or why the human female is the only mammal that carries lactation equipment on her torso years before it's needed to sustain newborn life. Are breasts secondary sexual characteristics that exist solely to feed offspring?

Maybe. Maybe not.

In fact, from the moment they first appear on the scene, our breasts continue to confound us. For starters, they fail to adhere to any predictable schedule. Breast development can begin as early as seven or eight years of age, or our "girls" can remain in hiding until our late teens or even twenties. As for how long they take to reach full development, no one knows that either. Plastic surgeons suggest that patients wait until they are at least twenty-two years old before undergoing most cosmetic breast surgeries, but many women will experience some breast development after that age.

Even after surgery, breast size is still in flux. They can still get bigger or shrink, and not just with pregnancy. One in five women will end up with bigger boobs after menopause (and I'm one of them).

Then there's the added complication that no two breasts are alike—even on the same person—which makes them more like sisters than twins.* They can rest up high, low, wide, or close together. They can be round on top or at the bottom, or start way back near the armpits. They can feel solid and dense or be more soft and pliable. Even areolas and nipples come in multiple shapes, colors, and sizes. And every shape and every placement is perfectly normal.

---

* To get a better idea of typical breast variations, visit Bratabase.com or 007b.com.

No one bra style or brand can be expected to flatter these multiple boob variations!

Not only are your breasts completely (and individually) unique, the changes your breasts experience are also unique. You might not go on a journey like mine, through dozens of different bra sizes. Your pair may require fewer (or more) trips to the lingerie store. How often and how much our breasts shift varies by individual. But I promise you, the shift does happen. Which is why a favorite bra can suddenly turn into an uncomfortable nightmare, sometimes almost overnight.

> No two breasts are alike, and most of us have a larger "leftie."

We don't all relate to our breasts in the same way, either. What I think about my pair will not reflect how you view your own. You and I can wear the same size bra but have totally different bra buying and fitting needs. Our lifestyles, occupations, and personalities may mean we have divergent bra needs and wear polar opposite looks.

Or they may not.

So, what else do we know about breasts? Researchers and bra fitters have observed some unusual breast trends over the last twenty years:

1. They are arriving sooner.

The age at which puberty begins continues to decline. Doctors are seeing breast development in girls as

> Earlier onset of puberty means breast development is starting in girls as young as seven years of age.

young as seven years old, and parents are now buying bras for their daughters long before they might have expected to do so.

2. They are getting bigger.

Obesity may be the cause for higher demand for plus-size bras. However, another significant change in breast size has been observed: the fastest growing segment of the bra industry is one targeted to the deep cup and small back market. Many younger women now wear bras with narrower bands (28-32) that are also higher up in the bra alphabet (F through K). Statistics show it's not due to an increase in teen breast plastic surgeries, either. These young girls are growing GG/H cups naturally.

3. More boys and men are growing breasts.

Both the surging hormones of puberty and the side effects of certain medications are causing more guys to develop breasts. While some men with gynecomastia (male breast growth) choose breast reduction surgery, others are embracing bra wear to support their new boobs.

* * *

So what can we, as consumers with breasts, be sure of? Only that our breasts are as unique as our DNA. And while some people's breasts present a wider range of possibilities, prices, and styles when bra shopping, many of our breast-bearing sisters and brothers must invest a little bit more time and money to find their sweet bra spot.

The key is to understand what works best for your unique set, and what you can expect a bra to do for your breasts.

Which brings me to our next topic . . . the myths and realities of bra wear.

CHAPTER 2

Bra Myths and Realities

NO ONE BELIEVES more in the power of bras than I do. They can transform my figure, improve my mood, and enhance the clothes I choose to wear. I love bras and their (almost) magical powers. But there are still a few things bras can't and won't do for my breasts.

Here are three common bra myths and reasons to ignore them:

MYTH #1
Bra wear prevents breasts from sagging.

As I mentioned in the previous chapter, our breasts are made up of fat, glandular tissue, nerves, arteries, and thin fibers that connect it all to the chest wall. The latter are called Cooper's ligaments, named after the doctor who discovered them while cutting up random cadavers in the name of science. Some believe that Cooper's Ligaments keep heavier breast tissue lifted, much like an internal bra. Others argue they are merely responsible for the curved shape of breasts.

No one knows whether these ligaments can be damaged or stretched out by physical activity or with age. What we do know is that skin elasticity breaks down over time, which inevitably leads to loose skin. Smoking, multiple pregnancies, and rapid weight gain and loss also destroy collagen, resulting in premature skin aging and sending your breasts further south before their time.

Beyond that, it's anyone's guess as to how to keep them perky and elevated. Most of us turn to bra wear to manage that trick. But there is no science behind claims that wearing a bra keeps your breasts standing at attention. A bra only prevents boob droop while you wear one.

MYTH #2
Bra wear causes breasts to sag.

This bra myth got some traction in 2013 when comments made by a French professor on a student radio show went viral. However, there is no peer-reviewed, published paper backing up his claim. There have been two other small studies claiming improved lift in larger-busted ladies after they ditched their bras, but their findings are less than conclusive because of the very narrow pool of participants involved. Some experts argue that propping up breasts with bras leads to something called Cooper's ligament atrophy, the theory being that, left to hold themselves up without "help," our girls become stronger. But these ligament strands can't be studied without cutting breasts open, so no one knows.

What the evidence does show is that genes, aging, and smoking have more power over the buoyancy of our boobs than our bras do.

MYTH #3
Bra wear is linked to breast cancer.

The authors of a 2005 book first proposed a connection between breast cancer and bra wear. But every reputable cancer charity and research organization has since debunked this theory, and in 2014, Seattle's Fred Hutchinson Cancer Research Center released findings that put this popular rumor to rest. There are certain lifestyle changes you can make to help lower your risk of breast cancer, but tossing out your bra isn't one of them.

Why wear a bra?
Most women won't leave home without boob support. A 2008 Consumer Reports poll reported that 80% of women wouldn't go out in public without a bra. I feel

the same way. It's not that I'm embarrassed to go without one or ashamed of my natural body. For me, it's like choosing the right footwear—it has a job to do and it damn well better look good while it does that job (oh yeah, and compliment my outfit too).

I wear bras to banish the bounce, maximize my workouts, and help my clothes look their best. However, we don't all wear bras for the same reasons. For one person, it's about keeping everything contained and restrained. Another might prefer basic nipple coverage. A third person may want uplift, sexy cleavage, or a flawless look under a T-shirt. Some of us wear bras to make certain activities easier or less burdensome, like running, nursing a baby, or keeping breast forms in place after mastectomy. And most of us have a drawer full of bras that do more than one of these jobs.

It's time to rethink all the negative bra talk. I believe bras are a blessing, not a curse. Why? Because of all the amazing things they can do, including:

- Improve posture

- Lift breasts off ribcage

- Limit bounce and take excess weight off back and shoulders

- Change the natural projection of breasts

- Alter breast size, either increasing or minimizing volume or cleavage

- ❖ Titillate and arouse a sexual partner

- ❖ Make you appear polished and professional in the workplace (according to surveys)

- ❖ Increase stamina and reduce pain when participating in athletic activities

- ❖ Flatter overall body shape under particular fashions

- ❖ Improve body image and self-confidence

The bottom line? Wearing a bra rocks! It should (and can) be a pleasurable experience, not one you hate or dread. And I promise you, each of the expectations I listed above are realistic. There are plenty of bra brands and styles on the market that do these things, and more.

In other words, the bras that will do what bras can do—improve our overall physical, mental, and sexual health—do exist. So what's keeping us from finding the right bras to satisfy our unique needs?

I've listed some of the most common bra-buying obstacles, as well as some tips to help you work around them:

1. Access to Retailers

Some people live miles from the nearest mall or department store or have limited bra-shopping choices in their area.

If this has been your experience, and you know what you want, you can ask your local store manager to stock your size or brand. Or you can contact one of the many boutiques now using Skype and Google to provide customers with personalized video bra fittings. If you're unsure of where to start, you can check out any number of helpful online lingerie blogs, websites, and study bra reviews to educate yourself on how to find the best intimate apparel.

2. Purchasing Power

Buying the right bra isn't about the size of your paycheck, it's about understanding the value of quality foundations. Rethinking your bra budget might open the door to a better fit and style of bra. On the flip side, you don't have to max out your bra budget for every bra in your lingerie wardrobe. Once you learn the basics of proper construction as well as what works best for you, it's easy to become a smart and thrifty bra shopper.

3. Ignoring Breast Shape and Figure

Not only can you not count on wearing one consistent bra size, but you also need to factor in your breast placement and body type when you choose a bra style. Are you short, tall, thin, athletic, or curvy? Where do your boobs rest on your chest (high, low, wide apart, or close-set)? Do you have narrow shoulders, an athletic build, or a short-waisted torso? Different bra brands and styles work better for different body types.

Embrace your individuality to make the search easier. More and more lingerie retailers are now catering to specific breast sizes, placements, and volume. Matching breast shape to a particular bra style can revolutionize how you approach bra buying. For more help finding the best bras for your build, check out the Beginner's Guide to Bra Styles (Chapter 6).

4. Sizing Outside Traditional Core Bra Sizes

Fall below an A or above a DD cup, or outside the 30- to 38-band range? Then you might not find what fits you within the core sizes that many retailers stock. While the full-bust and plus-size lingerie market has grown over the past decade, you may still need to hunt through the hangers for these sizes. The good news is that there are now dozens of brands dedicated to the needs of the petite, full, and plus-size bra market. You just have to know where to find them.

5. Having Unrealistic Expectations

The same bra you wear for yoga won't work under a button-down shirt or strapless evening gown. You wouldn't wear flip-flops with a cocktail dress, so it only makes sense that a single style of bra is not going to work with every type of fashion in your wardrobe. To figure out what bras your lingerie drawer should hold, make a list of your actual bra needs, including everyday, sports, special occasion, etc., before you start shopping. Don't forget, too, that fashions are designed to work with your foundations. If you haven't restocked your bra wardrobe in a couple of seasons, what you own may not work with more current clothing styles.

And don't forget that proper care extends the life of your lingerie. See Chapter 11 for recommended wash and care tips.

6. Neglecting Personal Style

I've bought plenty of bras that technically fit, but ended up stuffed into the back of my dresser drawer and never worn because they didn't compliment my wardrobe or lifestyle. You might be more sporty, fashion-forward, or traditional. Some of us like feminine frills while others prefer our undergarments less fussy. The good news is that there are thousands of bras to choose from in the vast world of lingerie. Yes, it's good to get out of your tired lingerie rut and experiment with new brands. However, what you choose should ultimately match your personal style. Otherwise, you'll waste precious time and money, and it'll end up in the back of your lingerie drawer.

7. Body Blame

There's an old saying that for women, there are only two sizes of breasts: either too big or too small. Maybe that's why it's easier to blame our bodies when we are uncomfortable in our bras. And with our ever-changing breast flesh, combined with inconsistent bra design, quality, and sizing, bra-related body shame can be very hard to avoid.

Some choose breast reductions, lifts, and implants to create the breasts that make them feel complete. However, even surgically altering your boobs won't make them perfect or stop them from continually changing. Accept that, at least when it comes to bra shopping, a false idea of perfection is counterproductive to your search for comfort and style. It's time to drop the negative talk and embrace your originality.

✻ ✻ ✻

The Bra Zone journey is one you'll be on the rest of your life—so you might as well enjoy it. The next few chapters will include more detailed ways to tackle some of the obstacles to bra bliss. But first, let's take a closer look at the major players in the bra industry, and how bras are made, sized, and sold.

CHAPTER 3

The State of Bras

SOME BRA HATERS claim that bras are some kind of modern day torture device invented by a sadistic (male) mad scientist. In reality, nothing could be further from the truth. At least three women—from three separate countries—filed for patents on bust-supporting designs in the late 1800s and early 1900s, each with a version of a new brassiere style designed to liberate women from the confines of the corset.

However, archeologists and historians would argue that prototypes of today's basic bra go back even further, to classical times. The recent discovery of a 600-year-old linen bra makes it clear that the bra isn't as contemporary as everyone assumes.

We have come a long way, though, from the days when Mary Phelps Jacob, a socialite, had her maid sew two silk hankies together and dubbed it a ground-breaking invention. Today's bras are made from a wide range of materials, from natural fabrics to man-made elastics, plastics, and rubberized foam. There are so many different types and styles of bras that it's hard to compare one brand to another.

And those intimate apparel brands, like breasts, are all different. There are big and small players, including many that sell products under a variety of different names. Perhaps this is because there's plenty of money to be made in making lingerie. And right now, no one appears to be making more of it than Victoria's Secret.

According to a 2015 Forbes report, Victoria's Secret (which includes Pink and LaSenza brands) represents nearly 62% of America's $9 billion lingerie market. That's a big chunk of the intimate apparel market—in fact, no other single brand comes near their market share in

> Over half of all bra design patents are registered to women.

the US. They have stores all over North America and Europe, sell online and via catalogs, and produce a highly rated televised lingerie fashion show every year.

Bra manufacturing is a highly specialized industry. Larger brands like Victoria's Secret have more clout when it comes to negotiating deals on the fabrics, laces, and the labor used to put all those pieces together. Theoretically, this allows Victoria's Secret to offer greater value at a particular price point. However, Victoria's Secret's range of bra styles and sizes, as the parent brand name implies, is limited. Their inventory is fixed on the core 32-40 bands and A-DDD cups, and leans toward more padded and cleavage-enhancing options. Their marketing is directed to college-aged and early twenty-something women, and is meant to appeal to the heterosexual male gaze. Their PINK label targets an even younger demographic. Their products can't meet every person's bra needs, budget, or fashion preferences.

But there is a big, beautiful bra world beyond this lingerie giant.

There are many companies that have been in the intimate apparel industry for far longer. These less famous names are found in department, boutique, and big-box stores. They may not operate brick-and-mortar outlets, but they have a vast worldwide reach. Walk down the aisles of any intimate apparel department and you'll find numerous labels owned by parent companies like Triumph, Wacoal, and Hanes,* to name only a few. Their combined products span a broader range of styles, sizes, and prices than you can imagine.

Today's bra market is much different than it was ten years ago, thanks to the digital age. Heavily financed lingerie start-ups are working hard to offer a different bra-buying experience, and over the last several years, dozens of different brands have hit the market. Clothing brands targeting women over thirty-five or those

---

* Wacoal subsidiaries include b.tempt'd, Elomi, Fantasie, Freya, Goddess, Huit, and Leia. Hanes owns Bali, Champion, Playtex, Shock Absorber, and Wonderbra.

focused on plus sizes are adding intimates to their apparel lines. Smaller companies and solo entrepreneurs now crowdsource funds to get up and running. You can choose from brands specializing in sizes from the petite to DD+ fit, vintage-inspired to high-tech construction, and androgynous to super sexy styles. There are more choices than ever before, and still room for new players to join the lingerie game.

The result is that it's getting easier to find foundations that fit your unique size and style needs. Bigger brands continue to dominate by buying up smaller labels to expand their consumer reach across continents. Thanks to the Internet, consumers aren't restricted to buying within their geographic location. They can shop directly from name brands or independent retailers anywhere in the world.

Here's what you should keep in mind on your bra search:

1. No two bras are alike (like breasts).

Why? Bras are made in different ways, using any number of components, or parts. Some can be molded on a machine, while others are exclusively cut-and-sewn. Designs utilize different materials, patterns, and methods of manufacturing. There can be anywhere from a few to several dozen components involved in one brand's manufacturing process. Some use wires, hooks, sliders (to adjust shoulder straps), and other embellishments like lace, bows, or trims. All these possibilities in quality, design, and manufacturing make a difference in how long and how well one bra holds up.

2. Every brand has its standards of correct measure and fit.

Bra sizing is not an exact science. You'll find fit charts utilizing the "Plus-4" method (adding 4 or more inches to the length of your underbust torso), while others look to your exact rib cage measurement for correct band size. There are multiple ways to determine size, from measuring above and across the bust (with or without your bra on), to calculating the width of each breast individually. One brand even offers half-cup bra sizes within the A-through-D cup range. As you go beyond DD+ cups, sizing criteria get more complicated and confusing. Bras above a G cup are more complex to fit.

3. A fitter with a cloth measuring tape is not the only way to determine size.

You can take a picture of yourself with an app, or answer questions and plug in your style needs on bra company and retail websites. Some manufacturers have sizing systems that leave out alphabet cup letters and band sizes altogether. Jockey recently came up with a ten-cup measuring system for their bras, utilizing plastic domes to gauge individual breast volume. And they're not the only company introducing unique sizing methods. HerRoom has developed a "universal" classification system to help consumers navigate similar sizes across multiple lingerie brands.

4. International bra sizing is inconsistent.

Different countries use different alphabetical/numerical systems. Take a look at the table of international bra sizes in the back of this book. Note that if you're anywhere outside the "core sizes" of A to D, you need to know what your cup size might be called in another country. And who knew that a AAA or AA was smaller than an A? Or that some brands multiply Ds instead of letting shoppers move up another letter (e.g., the rise of double D, triple D, and quad D sizing equivalent to E, F, and G cups). I'm baffled that the UK has no "I" and skips over that letter. Retailers don't use the exact same international bra size conversion chart. You have to research each brand to make sure you are speaking the same size language.

5. Different bra styles fit different breast shapes.

Not all styles are made to fit the same breast placement. Some work better for full on top, full on bottom, widely, or narrowly spaced breasts. Some bras are made to support heavy breasts, and others don't lift and separate as much. Those with breast implants or reconstructed breasts after mastectomy need designs that accommodate post-surgical scarring.

6. Brands specialize.

Some brands offer a vast range of sizes, and others carve out niche markets in areas of small bust, plus-size, full bust, maternity and nursing, sports, or post-mastectomy. All these designs have fit standards and challenges (for more, see Special Bra Fit Situations, Chapter 8). Brands also specialize in lower end, mid-price, or luxury items, and in specific fashion styles.

7. Brick-and-mortar stores can't stock every available bra.

Whether it's lack of inventory space or simply a focus on stocking what's new, shoppers can't expect to find every size and style of bra in one store. That's where online shopping becomes an advantage. You'll find more opportunities online if you know where to look.

8. Price matters.

Looking to only spend $10.99 on a bra? Know that the retailer markup is 50%, meaning the actual cost of this bra could be somewhere between $4 and $6. A $5 bra may not hold you up for long. The price of a bra represents more than just materials and labor. For some brands, it can mean months or years of research and development plus marketing and advertising costs. The value of one item may include more than what you see in fabric and lace.

9. There are new approaches to selling bras.

You can visit the mall or shop from online-only lingerie retailers. You'll also find bras available at small clothing boutiques, big box stores, adult shops, and sporting good retailers. There are companies ready to visit you at home or at the office to make it easier to fit and sell you a bra.

10. Brands are listening.

Social media platforms give brands a direct link to potential customers. You'll find active fashion bloggers posting product reviews and industry updates from seasonal trade shows. There are more ways to interact and provide feedback on sizing, styles, and fit—whether through brand-sponsored forums or independent blogs and lingerie and fashion communities.

✼ ✼ ✼

What's the future of the bra industry? New technologies combined with 3D printing could have consumers printing out their clothing, including lingerie, from home. But that's tomorrow, not today. For now, we need to figure out our best size within a more fluid Bra Zone and learn what the professionals mean by "perfect bra fit."

CHAPTER 4

Finding Your
Bra Zone Size

A FEW YEARS AGO I took a bra fitting class from one of the best fitters in the world, Fredericke Zappe. She runs the Eveden Fit School and has trained hundreds (if not thousands) of bra retailers and employees. So she clearly knows her stuff. When I asked her what she considers the most important key to fitting a client, her response was that you should first fit her "up here."

And with that, she pointed to her head.

Why the head and not the breasts? Because finding a bra that fits and functions beautifully is not about figuring out which letter or number covers your chest. It's about changing the way you think about dressing your breasts and embracing the way a great bra fits.

> **TBZ TIP** Don't own a cloth measuring tape? Try using a pair of ear buds. They measure 32 inches from the end of plug to where they split and 42 inches to the earpiece.

Finding your ideal Bra Zone means rethinking how much weight you give your bra size. That number-letter combination is merely a guideline, not gospel. However, that number-letter combination is still the best place to start, so this chapter will help you find the range of possibilities that best represents your starting size. We can then use that as a baseline as I guide you through the essential points of proper bra fit and toward the styles that will suit both your head and your chest.

When we talk about our breasts, we tend to talk about cup size. We classify our breasts according to letters of the alphabet, and I'm no different. I was a D, a DD, a C, and back to DD again. And whether it's two girlfriends having a conversation or an article on bra-fitting in a women's magazine or website, it's basically the same thing. "She's a D cup," or "I'm a C" is how most of us talk about boobs.

So you might be surprised to learn that this common reference point is not an accurate way to approach bra sizing. In reality, no person with breasts fits into just one number-letter combination all the time. And if you're hoping to find your ideal Bra Zone, labeling yourself as a specific cup size can be dangerous.

HERE ARE FIVE FACTS YOU SHOULD KNOW ABOUT BRA SIZING

1. No one sizing method works for everyone.

The age, stage, or size of one's bust translates into multiple requirements in support and styling. For instance, small and petite busts have different fit issues than deep cups or plus-size figures. Older boobs often aren't located in the same place as youthful or reconstructed breasts, nor do they move the same way. Even the size charts used by retailers aren't identical since every manufacturer relies on their own standard of measurement.

International sizing complicates things even further. Band size might be measured in centimeters, not inches. And the farther up you go in the cup alphabet, the more confusing it becomes, with different nations using different letters to represent the same thing. One look at the international guide in the appendix will confirm why converting number-letter sizes from other countries can get complicated.

2. Cup size is meaningless unless it is paired with a specific bra band number.

Bra cup letters refer to *breast volume across a specific band size.* Identical letters don't represent the same amount of volume as bands increase or decrease. In fact, the volume of a B cup on a 38 band is identical to the volume of a C cup on a 36 band and a D cup on a 34 band. Let me illustrate.

Let's say you have two identically sized cupcakes. One sits on a tiny tea saucer and the other on a large formal dinner plate.

The cupcake on the petite plate represents the volume of breast tissue on a 34-inch bra band and would be called a D cup. On the larger plate, which represents a 38-inch bra band, the same breast volume is referred to as a B cup. The cupcake (representing breast volume) takes up more space (larger cup) on a smaller plate. And the same breast volume takes up less space (smaller cup) when measured on a larger surface (band).

This is known as "sister sizing" in the bra industry. Here's a partial chart of some equivalent sister cup volumes; the following band/cup combinations represent identical breast volumes:

28F

    30E

        32D

            34C

                36B

                    38A

You can also think of the letter designation as representing the shape of a bra's underwire. The width of the underwire will increase as you move up bra band sizes to accommodate the same placement of breast volume. That means an A cup underwire will look very different on a 28-inch band than it will on a 38-inch band.

Here is why your knowledge of sister sizing is so crucial to bra fitting. If the cup fits you great but the band doesn't, you need to move to another cup size when you change the size of the band. Let's say you try on a bra and the band is too tight. Going UP a band size and DOWN a cup size will give you a better fit. On the other hand, if the band is too loose, you will go DOWN a band size and UP a cup size to make sure the cup has the identical volume. Got it? Don't worry; we'll go over this again. You will also find a complete chart of all sister sizes in Appendix A.

3. Beautiful bras above a D cup size are no longer hard to find.

A lot has changed since my struggle to find a decent first bra at the Bon Marché in the '60s. In 2016 it's a whole new bra world. Deep-cup brands (smaller bands with higher letter cups) are the fastest growing segment of the intimate apparel industry. One popular bra manufacturer recently told me that 32F is their best selling size. Multiple brands are targeting a younger demographic wearing D to J cups. (UK and

US brands also use different letters above the D cup to refer to same cup equivalency.)

So since a D cup is no longer that big a deal, there's no need to be afraid of trying on a G, HH, or J cup. The letter doesn't matter because the wire length and breast volume are the things you need to consider.

4. Your "perfect" size may not equal ideal bra fit.

There are a couple of reasons why a technically "correct" bra size doesn't always mean you've found the perfect bra for your frame. One involves physical factors like where your breasts rest on your chest, your body size, and/or the way your breasts are shaped by a certain bra style. The other has to do with a saying often applied to bra sizing: it's more art than science.

Art is subjective. A big part of the "art" of bra fit is consumer preference. You can try on two identically sized bras and one will feel great, and the other not so much. Given that you might wear more than one sister size across styles or brands, variations in construction, and personal preferences, it is easy to see why measurement is ONLY a starting point.

5. Bra fitters aren't the only ones who can unlock the mystery of your true bra size.

Yes, an expert in the field with access to multiple brands and sizes is a blessing. She can literally change your relationship to your breasts by helping you find what works best for you. But as mentioned in Chapter 2, you might not live near a store with an expert bra fitter. Sometimes it's simply impossible to meet face to face with an expert working in a well-stocked lingerie department. In that case, your best path to bra bliss is to do a bit of homework to figure out what you need.

Besides, not all bra fitters are created equal. Some have access to only a handful of the 200+ bra sizes on the market. And that's only taking into account the number of cups across every band length, not adding in variable bra styles.

WAYS TO DETERMINE BRA SIZE

So, with all of this information in mind, how can you determine your starting bra size? You've got several options beyond an in-store fitting.

1. In-Home or Office Bra-Fitting Services

Companies like Peach and Essential Bodywear employ stylists to help consumers find the perfect fit in the convenience of their home or office. Online retailer True&Co. uses a mobile bra-fitting try-on truck. Some of these companies have their own bra lines and/or carry well-known brands. You can also make Skype or video bra fitting appointments with independent lingerie boutiques and retailers (learn more about these services in Chapter 10.)

2. Answering Surveys

This method is available on numerous online retailer and brand websites such as HerRoom, Bare Necessities and True&Co. You take a quiz about your current bra fit and styles you prefer. Based on your answers, their software generates bra size and style recommendations. Knowing the points of bra fit listed in the next chapter will help you answer these questions more accurately and determine if you need to change your bra size or simply replace your current worn-out bras with newer models.

3. Phone Camera Bra-Measuring App

ThirdLove has developed an app that calculates your bra size based on photos taken with your cell phone (the app is free, and you remain fully dressed in the photos). Multiple bloggers have reviewed the app with mixed results. I couldn't get it to work for me, but that may be because of my advanced age and lack of patience with this kind of technology. Luckily, ThirdLove also makes it easy to figure out your size based on the way your current bra fits you.

4. Bra Size Calculating Models

Nearly every bra brand now has a website page where you can enter the dimensions of your chest to automatically calculate your size. There are also downloadable bra size calculator apps, but be warned: because of the variations in the way bra brands are sized, your results might be way off. If you know the brand you wish to buy, it's best to use their sizing method to find your best fit.

One more caveat: if you are on either end of the bra cup scale (AAA/AA/A or over a DD cup size), you might find it useful to consult bloggers and look for brands concentrating on your specific boob size and shape. You'll find a selection of these retailers and bloggers on either end of this bra cup spectrum in Chapter 10.

5. DIY Measuring Directions

If you're unsure of your bra size, either because of changes to your body or because you've never worn a bra before, you can use the standard old-school method of measurement. You'll need to slip into a soft cup or non-padded bra, plus have a cloth measuring tape, a mirror, and something to write down your results.

STEP 1: Wrap the measuring tape under your boobs at the smallest part of your rib cage. The tape should lie flat and be parallel to the ground. Write this number down. This represents your raw underbust measurement. Some bra fitters and brands will add one, two, or three or more inches to this number to figure your band size. One of the more well-known methods is called the "Plus-4" fitting standard. It recommends you add 4 inches to an even underbust number and 5 inches to an odd one. Keep these add-on methods in mind when we get to Step Four, below.

STEP 2: Wrap the tape over the widest part of your bust, over your boobs. Again, use the mirror to make sure the tape is straight and parallel to the floor. Write that number down. This represents your overbust measurement.

STEP 3: Cup size is determined by subtracting the raw underbust number in Step One from the overbust number found in Step Two. The difference between the two numbers is the basis for your cup size (see the chart on page 46).

STEP 4: Put your cup number together with the band size you found in Step 1 using either (a) the raw underbust measure (if odd, round up to next even number) or (b), the Plus-4 method. Either may work for you, or you may find yourself somewhere in between.

HERE'S AN EXAMPLE TO CLARIFY

Using the above formula, I measure 32 inches across my rib cage and 37 inches across my bust. Adding 0 inches to my rib measurement (using raw underbust number) puts me in a starting size of 32DD or E (37 - 32 = 5-inch difference). Because my back is fairly muscular, I prefer to wear the sister size of 34D or 34DD, depending on the bra style. The Plus-4 method would put me in a 36DD (the cup equivalent to a 34F). That may be my bra size in a brand using the Plus-4 method of fit. These four "sizes" belong in my personal Bra Zone.

DETERMINING CUP SIZE USING DIY MEASURING

Difference	US	EU	UK
Less than ½ inch	AAA		AAA
½ – 1 inch	AA	AA	AA
1 inch	A	A	A
2 inches	B	B	B
3 inches	C	C	C
4 inches	D	D	D
5 inches	DD/E	E	DD
6 inches	DDD/F	F	E
7 inches	DDDD/G	G	F
8 inches	DDDDD/H	H	FF
9 inches	DDDDDD/I	I	G
10 inches	J	J	GG
11 inches	K	K	H
12 inches	L	L	HH
13 inches	M	M	J
14 inches	N	N	JJ
15 inches	O	O	K

If you find the whole measuring thing confusing, you are not alone. But there is another excellent reason to know these overbust and underbust numbers: you'll have a concrete way to measure changes in your body, and an idea of whether it's time to invest in new foundations.

Now you will learn how to tweak the number-letter combo by using the points of correct bra fit. Like shoe shopping, you need to try on a bra to find out if you like the way it looks and feels on you. The next chapter gives you the tools to figure out whether you need to move up or down a band size, cup size, or both.

CHAPTER 5

Bra Fit Basics and the Rules of Fit

MOST PEOPLE BELIEVE that once they learn their "right" size, they'll find the perfect bra fit. However, while that's a good place to start, as we learned in the last chapter, size alone doesn't paint the whole bra picture.

It's easy to find a bra that technically fits me. But the way it looks under my shirt or how it molds my boobs may be unappealing to me. It may even be uncomfortable since my skin isn't as tight or firm as it used to be.

Choosing a bra is like choosing footwear. Just because a pair of shoes are my size doesn't mean I want to wear them out of the store. The best bra fit for you starts with your correct size (in any one brand), but also takes into account the style that you prefer for

> **TBZ TIP**   Always fit a new bra to the outermost hook of the band. As the elastic stretches out over time you can move to inner hooks to tighten the band.

your breast and body shape, plus any other personal preferences.

However, since we have to start somewhere in the quest to determine your Bra Zone, we'll begin with the basics of proper bra fit. To be clear, I am talking about fitting into a cup-sized bra, not bras that come in small, medium, large, etc. Those alpha sizes are a whole other fitting issue that also changes across multiple brands.

Understanding bra fit begins with knowing basic bra terminology. That way you will know what to ask about when and if you have specific problems related to construction.

BASIC BRA CONSTRUCTION VOCABULARY

Band: The part of the bra that holds up your breasts. According to experts, it is meant to hold 80% to 90% of your breast weight. Bands are typically made of flexible, elastic materials. They come in multiple widths, can be cut as a straight line, or curve up in the center. Some bands hook up in front, too. Longline bras have bands that extend from a few inches to your waist.

Nubian Skin Classic Lace Push-Up Bra

Boning: Can be added underneath the arms onto the side wings of the band to offer extra support and structure.

Cups: Can be wired, non-wired, cut and sewn with multiple seams, padded, or machine made ("molded" by a machine). Some styles add an inner "side sling" to shape the breast tissue and bring it forward. Cup shape determines the way the breasts are lifted and in what direction they are projected. In general, the more seams in a cup, the better support it will provide.

Embellishments: Anything and everything you can think of that can be added to a bra: bows in the center, lace bits along the edge or cups, fancy strap details, lace overlays, etc.

True&Co. Merced Front Close T-Back Bra

Gore: This is the very center part of a bra, where the two cups meet. This area can be short, tall, small, or wider set, depending on the style.

Hooks: Come in singles, doubles, triples, or more. Multiple hooks allow the bra wearer to shorten the band (again, the most important part of the bra in terms of support) as elastic wears. This extends the life of the bra and ensures a longer and superior fit. Some bra styles hook in front and are called front closure bras.

Sliders: The plastic or metal found on bra straps that allow you to shorten or lengthen them.

Straps: The job of your straps is not to support your breasts but to keep the band in place (bra fitters claim straps account for only 10% to 20% of the load lifted).

They can be thick or thin, set close or far apart, and can even be heavily padded. Some straps are removable, criss-cross in back, or can hook together. Many bras have straps that don't adjust. All these choices in strap placement and modification are important to remember as you decide what you want a bra to do for you.

Wings: These are the sides of the bra that wrap around toward the back. You want to pay attention to wing construction and fabric, especially if one of your bra fit issues is excess back fat (see troubleshooting and customizing your bra experience in Chapter 7, Hacks and Fixes).

Wire: Not all bras feature wires. Wires can be of different lengths and come in multiple shapes, from U to J models. They are contained in a casing and some bra manufactures may wrap them in extra material to provide added comfort. The way these wires are secured to a bra can vary.

The wires separate the breast and rest against the body, providing stability and keeping the breasts where you want them. You'll want to consider length of the cup wire if you have a shorter torso.

* * *

You can see from this list that bras can be made with anything from a few to hundreds of components.

Claudette En Dentelle Underwire Demi Bra

Other variables include the fabric's thread count, the quality of the lace (whether the cup is made on a machine or hand sewn), and elasticity. Even the number of stitches used on a particular garment gives you a clue about what went into its construction.

Now that we have a common language, we have one more thing to cover before we get to proper bra fit: how to put on a bra. That may seem like a ridiculous thing to cover in detail, but it's actually important. Bras are designed to fit a certain way, but they only work if you put them on properly.

HOW TO PUT ON A BRA

There are two different ways to put on a bra that hooks up in back.*

The first is the one recommended by bra fitters and manufacturers.

STEP 1: Hold the bra in front of you.

STEP 2: Put your arms through the straps.

STEP 3: Bend forward to let your breasts fall into the cups.

STEP 4: Hook the band up behind you (on the outermost hook if it's a new bra).

The second way to put on a back-close bra is a little easier.

STEP 1: Hook it up in front—or to the side—above your waist.

STEP 2: Gently spin the bra around your body until the hook is in the back.

STEP 3: Put your arms through the straps and adjust breast tissue into cups.

Bra fitters don't recommend this second method because it stresses and stretches out the elastic of the band. But I'll be honest: it's how I put on my bras. I

*To put on a front closing bra, put arms through straps and hook in front. Why aren't all bras made with front hooks? Because one central hook can limit bra design and flexibility in adjusting band length over time.

can't seem to train my brain to do it any other way. (My bad.) Those with arm or shoulder mobility issues may have no other choice than to hook in front and turn their bras around to the back.

No matter how you hook up your bra, once you have it on you also need to do the following:

Swoop and scoop your breast tissue into the cups.

Reach toward the back of the bra cup and move your boob flesh to the front. This helps to make sure that all the breast tissue is inside the cup and not resting outside the frame, possibly pinched by wires (ouch).

Adjust straps so that they are the proper length.

Depending on your body frame, a brand's straps might be too short or too long. If the straps are set too far apart, they might fall off your shoulders (see Chapter 7, Hacks and Fixes.)

SIX RULES OF PROPER BRA FIT

Now that the bra is on, you can follow these six rules to decide whether the size is right for you.

1. The band should be snug, but not too snug.

Any new bra band will feel tighter than a worn out model you've been wearing for months, or even years. But it shouldn't be so tight that it digs into your skin. Some people may have more muscle, softer tissue, or sensitive skin that makes wearing a band that matches their size uncomfortable. That's okay, too. Try another band size up or down to find what feels right.

2. The center gore should rest flush against the breastbone.

This is also called "tacking" against the breastbone. The center gore should not pull away from your body. If it does, you should move up a cup size.

3. The bra wires should sit on your ribcage, not on breast flesh.

Stand sideways in front of the mirror to see if the wire follows the natural crease or shape of your breast (also called the breast root). If any part of the wire is sitting on tissue (after you've done the swoop and scoop thing), the cup is too small.

4. The front and back of the band should be even, at the same height, and parallel to the floor.

Look at yourself sideways in a full-length mirror. If the band is riding up in back, you should try a larger band (but remember to go down a cup size). If the band is too loose, try one band size smaller and go up a cup size.

5. Your breast tissue should be fully contained in the cups.

Your boobs should not be spilling out over the top. There shouldn't be empty space in the cups either, or puckered or wrinkled lace. If there's space in the cups, try a smaller cup. If your girls are spilling out (the famous quad boob look), try going up a size. And if you're going crazy trying to fit two very different-sized breasts into one bra (totes normal), check the tips in Chapter 7.

6. Your straps should not be digging into or falling off of your shoulders.

Some bra styles feature wide-set straps, which might not work if you have narrow shoulders. In that case, you may have a bra style problem more than a band/cup size issue.

❊ ❊ ❊

Even when a bra meets all six of these fit rules, you may still not like the way it looks on your boobs or body. That's why it's important to know about different bra styles, their pros and cons, and what fashion problems they solve. In the next chapter we'll take a closer look at the variety of bra styles available to help you determine which one(s) are right for you. And later on, we'll talk about troubleshooting specific bra problems and customizing your bra fit.

I know it may all sound complicated, but it really isn't. Once you learn to spot these easy bra cheats you'll know quickly which bra fits better than another. Now that you understand basic bra construction and know how you like bras to fit on you, finding your perfect bra will be as easy as picking out a new pair of shoes (ha).

CHAPTER 6

Beginner's Guide to Bra Styles

IT'S EASY TO GET LOST in the world of bra styles. For starters, there are a lot of them. The terms used to name them can refer to the materials used to make them, like underwire or push-up padding, or the design of a bra, like a bralette, demi-cup, or strapless. There are even bras that are named entirely for their purpose, like back smoothing, sports, nursing, and post-mastectomy bras.

And if that's not enough, most bras do more than one thing!

Compare the following True & Co. underwire, seamless spacer bra with the Little Bra Company plunge push-up lace bra. One covers more of the breast and provides a smooth look under your clothing. The other

True&Co. A Space Girl's Dream Full Coverage Seamless T-shirt Bra

The Little Bra Company Lucia Deep Plunge Push-up Bra

pushes breast tissue up from the bottom, creates cleavage, and has a less even surface. These two bras have different functions and create totally different looks.

There are so many bra styles out there, and when you combine them with different breast shapes, how do you know which ones will work best for your chest? Let's start with a visual demonstration.

Think of bras like the cupcake tins used to make these delightful desserts . . . and the cupcakes as boobs. Both tins have the same shape. The only difference in the size of the cupcake is the volume put into the tin. The first cupcake, with larger amount of batter, rises higher in the tin, creating a muffin-top. The other tin holds less volume and lies flat in the same size circular container.

But what if you had different shaped cupcake tins? The smaller amount of batter in a tinier tin would create a higher muffin top. More volume in an even bigger cupcake tin would make it look flat. It's the same thing with breast volume and bra styles. You can change the look of your breasts by the style of bra you wear.

The right bra style sculpts your breasts into the shape that makes them fit and look their best under a specific piece of clothing. Let's say I'm wearing a round scoop-neck T-shirt during the day and switch to a deep plunge V-neck top at night. Both fashion choices require different bra styles to look their best.

The best way to understand bra styles is to start by asking what question a bra can answer for you. Do you want a bra that will create cleavage or prevent it? Do you need to have your breasts centered and pointed up front? Do you want your boobs hoisted higher up under a strapless evening dress? Do you need them strapped down when you're running, or want a nip-free look under a tight tee? Every bra style will answer one or more of these questions, along with many others.

One caveat before we get started. By explaining what these different bra styles do, my intent is not to restrict what you wear. You get to decide what works for you. Some materials and designs are better suited to holding up smaller or larger busts, or creating certain breast shapes, or disappearing under clothing. By explaining these differences, my goal is not to limit your choices, but to point out a realm of possibilities. If you dig a quad-boob look, go for it!

TO WIRE OR NOT TO WIRE?

A well-made underwire bra can provide superior and comfortable support for any sized bust, but especially fuller ones. Unfortunately, many people hate wearing them. Some don't like how the wires sometimes poke through the fabric and stab them. Others don't like the way the wires rub against their skin. But many reasons why underwire bras can be uncomfortable can be solved by choosing the correct shape or size of wire for the length of your body or breast root. Or it could be that the casement (layer of fabric around the wire) is too thin, and one with extra padding would feel better. The way you wash and care for your bras (see Chapter 11) can help prevent wires from breaking free of casings, too.

The good news is that there are plenty of great wire-free options now on the market that you should explore. And they're not just for smaller cup sizes either. New fabrics and innovative designs make it possible to lift and separate without all that hardware, making non-wired bras another viable option to consider when shopping.

The second thing to look for in a bra, wireless or not, is whether the cups are seamless or have seams. Bras generally fall into two categories: those with cups that are cut and sewn (seamed), and those that are not. The latter are often referred to as T-shirt, contour, or molded cup bras (because a machine "molds" the cup). When you're not wearing them, they look like the boobs are still in them.

I've been in lingerie departments where there were zero seamed cup bras on display. The only styles available were made of heavier foam material. That's too bad. In general, the more seams on a bra, the more shaping and support for breasts—no matter the band and cup size combination. Bras with multiple seams may also contain "molded" foam parts to better manipulate breasts into desired shapes.

Seamless bras have their advantages, in that they work well under many types of clothing, especially clingy knits and T-shirts. But it's good to have both kinds in your bra wardrobe since they answer different foundation questions (for more on building a bra wardrobe, see Chapter 11.)

PROS AND CONS OF
SEAMLESS VS. SEAMED STYLES

SEAMLESS T-SHIRT and CONTOUR CUP BRAS

Today's seamless bras come in underwire and wireless styles, with plunging necklines, graduated push-ups, and in strapless designs.

☛ **Pros** Invisible, for the most part, under T-shirts and clingy tight tops. Foam lining also helps with any high beam nipple issues.

☛ **Cons** May feel bulky and/or add unwanted padding. Women with less full-on-top breasts may not fill the top half of the rounded cup shape.

Another advancement in T-shirt bras are those made of "spacer" material, essentially two layers with space in between that makes the bra lighter and more breathable. It's less bulky than a contour bra but may not provide as much nipple coverage.

Nubian Skin Essential Underwire T-shirt Bra

Seamless bras can also be made of lightweight memory foam. The fabric conforms to the shape of your breast, and is more pliable and flexible than stiffer, contour T-shirt bras.

CUT-AND-SEWN CUP BRAS

These bras can be made from several kinds of materials, and the cups can be constructed of two, three, or even four parts. As you'll see below, whether your seams are horizontal or vertical changes the alignment of your breast tissue.

↬ **Pros** More seams generally means more structural support, so this style of bra is a better choice for those who want the same.

↬ **Cons** Less nipple coverage and may look less smooth under clingy fabrics.

Elila Glamour Multi-Seamed Embroidery Underwire Bra

Below are the four most common bra styles and the fashion problems they solve. (Special bra fit situations like first, maternity, or post-mastectomy are covered in Chapter 8; information on sports bras is reviewed in Chapter 9.)

FULL COVERAGE

As the name implies, this bra style provides the most support and coverage of your boobs. It's your wardrobe "workhorse" that has straps that are set closer together, the center gore is higher, and it may feature side slings to lift and bring your breasts to the front. Full coverage bras can have additional features like back smoothing wings (see below).

≈ **Pros** Great for almost every bust, and especially full and heavier busts as maximum coverage keeps everything in place.

≈ **Cons** Bra will be visible under plunging, deep scoop neck, or low-cut necklines.

Sculptresse by Panache Rosie Full Cup Underwire Bra

PLUNGE

This style is cut with a lower and deeper gore, and the wire has more of a "J" shape, meaning it's shorter in front. The cups have more of a triangle than rounded shape.

↣ **Pros** Great for wider-set breasts as cut of cups brings breasts closer together. Also ideal choice to wear under deep plunging necklines, and a wonderful way to create boobs-pushed-together-type cleavage

↣ **Cons** Those with closer-set breasts or with more volume on top may feel like they are spilling out of this style.

Curvy Couture Animal Attraction Perfect Plunge Multi-Way Bra

BALCONETTE, BALCONET, and/or BALCONY

The name pretty much sums it up—think of this style as "putting your boobs up in the balcony." The upper part of the breast is more exposed, the center gore is lower, and the design lifts and separates (unlike the plunge). Straps are set wider apart than with the full-coverage style but not as far apart as with the demi-cup below.

☙ Pros This is a good choice for those with shallower breasts or who want to center their boobs on their chest.

☙ Cons If your breasts are already fairly full on top, the danger is that you might spill out over the top of the cups, and create quad-boob look. Those with heavier breasts may not find as much support in this style. Wider-set straps may be an issue for those with short torsos or sloping shoulders.

Cleo by Panache Kali Balconnnet bra

Simone Pérèle Delice Demi Cup Bra

DEMI-CUP

You'll recognize this bra by its vertical seam on the front of each cup. The straps are set even wider apart than the balconette, and the top of the cups look as if they are cut straight across the bust. This half-cup style bra has shorter wires and less material exposes more of your chest. The vertical seam placement lifts and centers your breasts.

☙ **Pros** Great for low-cut tops and a good option for when you're striving for less "creasage" in your cleavage. Breasts with less upper volume may benefit from the sexier push-up look this style creates, without any padding. Demi bras are available for all bust sizes.

☙ **Cons** Wider-set straps can be a challenge for those with narrow shoulders. The more open décolletage might not feel like enough coverage.

PROS AND CONS OF ADDITIONAL STYLES

Other styles you should know about, along with some of the wardrobe problems they solve (in alphabetical order):

ADHESIVE BRA

Made of silicone material with adhesive backing. Designed as two separate cups that hook together, allowing the wearer to adjust height or spacing of their breasts. Most adhesive bras can be worn multiple times.

☞ Pros Great for cleavage creation, nipple control, and support under backless or low-back fashions.

☞ Cons Best for smaller or higher set breasts, since adhesive won't hold as well under greater weight or size.

BANDEAU BRA

Made for less bust support and in smaller sizes because it is less structured, with one seam in the middle and a wireless cup.

☞ Pros It can be worn in place of a strapless bra or be a super cute casual bra under loose tops with wide sleeve openings.

☞ Cons Flattens out breasts, and provides zero support for heavier breasts whose weight can drag bra downward.

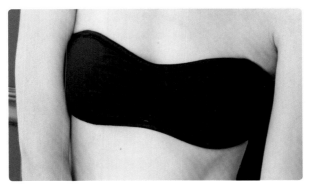

Lula Lu Petites Bandeau Bra

Curvy Couture Flawless Contour Wire-Free Bra

BACK-SMOOTHING BRA

Any bra where the band is designed to cover more of your back with smooth or laser-cut seamed "wings." Back band and straps may create a "ballet' or "U" shape. The extra material and shape smoothes out any soft skin issues, and the band doesn't dig into the skin.

❧ **Pros** Lessens appearance of lumps and bumps around back band.

❧ **Cons** May appear too utilitarian for some tastes.

BRALETTE

Unwired bra typically made of soft material or stretch lace. Many times there are no adjustable straps or bands and the bra is put on over your head. It can be worn under any type of top, or serve as a sleep bra. Not just for petite cups either, as more brands are offering them in full bust sizes.

Tia Lyn Core Bralette

☙ Pros Always good to have an unstructured option in your bra wardrobe.

☙ Cons Little support and structure when worn under certain clothes.

CONVERTIBLE BRA

This style lets you convert straps from a standard position and cross them in back, or remove them entirely and wear it as a strapless style (see also Strapless, page 75). Some brands include a small clip on the back of each bra strap that allows you to connect them together (see Racer-Back, page 74).

☙ Pros Gives you more fashion options in one bra.

☙ Cons Straps usually set wider apart which can be difficult for smaller torsos. Strapless option may not be as comfortable as that found in a bra designed specifically to be worn without any straps.

FRONT-CLOSE BRA

Bras that close in front.

🖙 **Pros** Works well for wider-set breasts as cups bring tissue together. Best to wear underneath racerback style fashions. Lessens pain of those with arm and shoulder mobility issues.

🖙 **Cons** Can create too much cleavage for larger, heavier, or closer-set breasts. You won't be able to adjust the length of the band as the bra ages and stretches out.

LONGLINE

This style is making a fashion comeback thanks to the vintage, retro, and pin-up revival. The bra has a wider band that can reach an inch or more below the ribcage.

🖙 **Pros** Provides more stability and support for larger breasts (thanks to wider bands).

🖙 **Cons** Those with a shorter waist or higher tummies may find this style uncomfortable.

Elila Lace Longline Strapless Bra

True&Co. Seaside Unlined Longline Bra

MINIMIZER

Designed to minimize (hence the name) breast tissue by flattening it out. It makes your boobs stick out less by spreading out tissue over the breadth of your chest. There's a great deal of argument over this bra style among fitters and some bloggers since some think the design doesn't do as good a job as a multi-seam bra in lifting and sculpting a fuller chest. I say if you like the look, go for it.

☞ Pros Reduces forward breast projection.

☞ Cons Spreads breast tissue across chest, which may not look best under all fashions.

PADDED

Any bra style made with extra padding. The padding can cover the entire cup, or be graduated, or it can simply be a thicker T-shirt or contour bra.

☞ Pros Great for nipple coverage.

☞ Cons May add bulk where you don't want it.

PUSH-UPS

Bras with sewn-in or removable pads to either (a) add volume to your cup size or (b), push your breasts up from the bottom or sides of the cup. Push-up bras are available in all cup sizes.

The Little Bra Company Mercedes Demi Push-Up Bra

Tutti Rouge Jessica Plunge Bra w/ Removable Cookies

 Pros Adds volume to your breasts and can create cleavage.

 Cons Adds volume to your breasts and can create cleavage.

QUARTER-CUP or OPEN-CUP BRA

The quarter-cup is lower than the demi and does not cover the nipple, although it might include some lace to lightly cover nipples.

 Pros Very sexy, and surprisingly supportive, as breasts are framed and lifted.

 Cons Will not support larger and heavier breasts.

RACER-BACK

Also often called a T-back bra. See Front-Close Bra style, page 72.

SLEEP BRA

Any bra you decide to sleep in, really. Most sleep bras are made of lightweight, breathable, unstructured fabric, without any wires, and may hook in front.

 Pros Keeps your breasts in one place when you are sleeping.

 Cons May feel too restricting.

STRAPLESS

Can be made of lace or contour cups, come in short or longline styles, and are available in push-up styles. Longline strapless bras (sometimes called bustiers) provide better support for heavier or fuller busts. Many strapless bras come with optional straps that allow you to crisscross or convert straps in other ways. Since all of the support in a strapless bra comes from the band, it's best to buy one that is snug around your ribcage.

≈ Pros Good to wear with lightweight summer dresses and strapless cocktail and formal fashions.

≈ Cons Cup shapes differ, so a tricky style to find correct fit. You may need to go down a band and up a cup

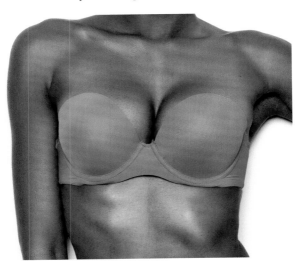

Nubian Skin Cinnamon Bun Convertible Underwire Strapless Bra

size. Look for bras that include a silicone band edge so band stays in place. Always test a strapless under your formal dress before buying.

* * *

The styles listed above are the most common options you'll find in stores and online. In the next chapter, we'll tackle some specific bra fitting challenges and ways to alleviate common bra problems using innovative bra add-ons. That way you can customize your bras to better meet every wardrobe need.

CHAPTER 7

Hacks and Fixes

NOW THAT YOU have a better understanding of bra styles and how they shape your breasts, you can look for the styles that work best for you. That means refining your bra search to look for style elements that best suit your bust. You've learned some basic troubleshooting from the fitting and sizing chapter, including how issues like "double boob" and "wrinkled cups" can be fixed by choosing a bigger or smaller cup size; and how bands riding up the back can be traced to a band that's too big or a bra that's lost its original elasticity. Now we're going to take our quest for the perfect fit one step further by looking at some other common bra problems. We'll also explore some potential solutions, including a range of amazing new bra add-ons and accessories that may get you thinking "outside the bra."

CHALLENGE: Bra Band Too Long (or Small Ribcage)

SOLUTION: If your problem is that your cups fit great, but the band is too long (or has stretched out over time), you can purchase a bra band shortener, like the Rixie Clip, to take up the slack. This nifty clip comes in three colors and four hook sizes.

Rixie Clip: Available in Four Band Width Sizes

CHALLENGE: Bra Band Too Short (or Broad Back)

SOLUTION: Band sizes span from 28 to 50 across different bra brands. But that doesn't mean all bras are available in every size. You can, however, buy bra band extenders that allow you to add inches to any bra that fits in every other way except around your unique ribcage. And they're available in double, triple, and even quad-hook combinations and multiple colors.

CHALLENGE: Bra Band Digging into High Stomach

SOLUTION: Shop for bras that have bands with an arched center gore. Avoid longline styles.

Panache Andorra Lace Full Cup Bra

CHALLENGE: Bra Strap Shoulder Pain / Strap Slippage

SOLUTION: When was the last time you adjusted your bra straps? If that doesn't solve the problem, remember that not all bra straps are created equal. Some dig into your shoulders, slip off, or even irritate your skin, whatever your bra size. If you're more full-busted, you can look for padded adjustable straps in some bra brands (like Elila). You can also buy nifty little fabric or silicone stay-in-place bra strap shoulder cushions to keep your straps where they belong. (For solutions for sloping shoulders, see page 81.)

CHALLENGE: Cleavage Creation

SOLUTION: Plunge and/or push-up bras are the easiest way to bring breasts together. But remember, not all push-up bras are the same. Some have padding located at the sides, others at the bottom of the cup, and some have "graduated" padding. Decide whether you need more volume added from the sides (for more widely spaced breasts) or from below (which boosts more shallow breast tissue).

CHALLENGE: Concealing Nipples or "High Beams"

SOLUTION: Worried about nipping out but don't want to wear a T-shirt bra under every outfit? While it's normal for some nipples to always be at attention, if it makes you uncomfortable, invest in nipple covers. From neutral skin tones to options in every color and shape imaginable, you'll always feel secure. You can also wear them when going bra-free. There are multiple brands on the market to choose from, including nipple covers without adhesive for those who have skin allergies.

CHALLENGE: Heavy Breast Tissue

SOLUTION: Choose multi-seamed bras with straps that form more of a "U" shape in back or with "Ballet" back. These are structured to handle heavier loads. Stay away from cups made of stretch lace fabrics that provide less support. You don't have to give up lacy designs, though, as many larger cup brands use solid lace fabrics to keep boobs elevated.

CHALLENGE: Narrow or Sloping Shoulders

SOLUTION: Choose racerback styles or look for bras that have more of a "U" back shape (the straps are located closer to the center of the back band). Many back-smoothing-styled bras also have closer set-in straps.

Alternatively, you can convert any conventional bra into a racerback style by using separate bra clips, strap converters, or holders. You simply attach a clip or extra strap to both straps to connect them in the middle. Keep in mind any arm flexibility or mobility issues you might have before buying a specific size or style of strap converter.

The DIY version of this is to use a large paperclip to connect your bra straps together. (See also Bra Strap Slippage, page 79.)

CHALLENGE: Uneven Breasts

SOLUTION: Everyone has two different size breasts on their chest, and sometimes that difference is more pronounced. In some cases, choosing a stretch lace bra to better accommodate two different breast shapes can solve the problem. This doesn't always work for larger, heavier breasts, as the stretch material may not provide enough support.

Another option is a push-up bra style with removable pads, so you can keep the padding only on the side where it's most needed.

You can also buy separate bra inserts and enhancers that slip inside your bra cup and stay in place. Referred to as "chicken cutlets" in the lingerie trade, they are made of fabric, foam, or silicone, come in a variety of sizes and styles, and serve as a great way to achieve extra volume or lift. Depending on their shape, these are also useful after some breast cancer surgeries (lumpectomies) to even out lost volume on one side.

CHALLENGE: Under Boob Sweat or Skin Irritations
SOLUTION: There are multiple products on the market known as "bra liners." They are made to stay in place underneath your bra band to help keep you cool and irritation free.

CHALLENGE: Too Long Straps
SOLUTION: Are your straps too long for your torso? Some intimate apparel retailers and fine department stores will tailor bra straps for their customers. But there is another store-bought solution to the problem, especially if you have a favorite bra that still fits great but the straps have worn out to the point where they're longer than you'd like. Strap Saver shortens up too long or worn out straps, and it can also be used on bra cup-sized bathing suit straps.

The Strap Saver: Available in Multiple Widths and Colors

CHALLENGE: Worry Over Wardrobe Malfunctions

SOLUTION: Your personal definition of perfect fit, fashion, and support may be the absence of any wardrobe malfunction. If you're looking for a worry-free foundation experience, you might consider keeping these extras in your Bra Zone wardrobe:

Clear Bra Straps: These can be tricky to use, but are worth keeping in your bra first-aid kit. I've substituted them for darker bra straps or added them to a strapless bra. You'll find a surprising number of uses for them once you own a pair.

Fashion Tape: How do celebrities on the Red Carpet keep their extreme plunging necklines from falling open? They rely on double-stick skin and fabric tape. There are multiple brands available and they are great for quick fixes on hemlines, covering broken bra wires, or other possible wardrobe fails. This easy fashion fix comes in many shapes and sizes, and fits into any small evening purse or wallet.

❊ ❊ ❊

Even with all these nifty little gadgets and tricks, there are still going to be times in your life when you have to throw out everything you know and start from scratch. That's certainly what happened to me in puberty, pregnancy (all three of them), and after menopause. Breasts change over time and under specific circumstances. The next chapter deals with bra fitting situations where finding the right style and size of bra can be even more challenging.

CHAPTER 8

Special Bra Fit Situations

IT MIGHT SEEM LIKE every time you have to replace a bra qualifies as a special fit situation. If you're like me, you do so when your bra wears out, or because your body or breasts have changed. I've also spent hours searching for the perfect foundation to wear under a special occasion dress.

However, there are times in one's life when buying a bra is even more challenging than usual. It could happen thanks to hormonal changes that come with age or pregnancy, or when breasts are altered by disease or by choice through cosmetic breast surgery. Men also wear bras, either because they want to or they need support for their own chests.

The following are a few tips for dealing with special bra fit situations. You'll find additional shopping resources, lingerie brand recommendations, and blog resources for these specific issues listed in Appendix C.

ADOLESCENCE/PUBERTY

Girls can be either excited or appalled by the prospect of wearing a bra. That means parents and caregivers need to be extra sensitive to their daughter's needs and wants.

Some girls begin to grow breast buds as early as seven years of age, while others don't develop until their late teens. One girl may be moving up through the cup size alphabet at breakneck speed, while everyone else in her class is still wearing camisoles. Hormonal surges make first-time bra wearers very self-conscious—plus the process of breast development is often physically painful and skin is easily irritated. Some young girls may prefer to wear crop tops, bandeaus, or soft bralettes to stay as comfortable as possible, and to avoid that "I'm wearing a bra" look. Others will gravitate toward padded molded cups to cover the nipples they're suddenly embarrassed by.

Do as much homework as possible on styles, sizes, and brands, and remind your daughter that she will be more comfortable with this new part of her anatomy when she takes charge of how to dress herself. Make sure she has plenty of sports bras so she can continue

Yellowberry Chickadee Bra

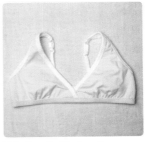
Yellowberry Budding Berry Bra

to participate in her favorite athletic activities without feeling uncomfortable or self-conscious. It's also a good time to teach her bra wear and care basics. Try to show her ways to accept her developing breasts and share methods that will help her make them less of a hindrance.

PREGNANCY AND NURSING

There's no need to change your fashion style when you get pregnant or when you are in need of nursing bras. Maternity lingerie brands are expanding their offerings to include bras, sports bras, shapewear, nightwear, and swimwear.

Nursing bras are available at every price point and can range from basic utilitarian fabrics and colors to sexy, racy designs—plus everything in between. Most are constructed of soft, breathable materials, with an extra pocket or padding for leakage, plus one-handed

Cake Lingerie Banana Parfait Flexi-Wire Lace Nursing Bra

access at the top of the cups for ease of feeding. They are available in both underwire and wire-free styles. (There is no medical evidence that underwire nursing bras cause mastitis—a painful inflammation that interferes with breast milk production. But wearing a nursing bra that is too small or too tight can make this problem worse.) If you plan to use a breast pump, there are specific bras/bandeaus and convertible nursing bras that make it easier, and some that accommodate both pumping and nursing.

Don't shop for nursing bras until you're near the end of your third trimester. Look for brands that give you the option of adjusting both the band and the cups, since initial milk production is erratic and you can find your breasts engorged during this time. You may also want a sleep bra or camisole with a drop cup handy for nighttime feedings.

> The most challenging bra fit situation is often your wedding day. Make sure to consider available bra style options before you invest in a dress.

POST-BREASTFEEDING AND PREGNANCY

Women can be anxious to reclaim their breasts from baby after breastfeeding for months or even years. They might find that their breast volume has changed and their boobs are less full on top or lower on their torso. Others retain more fullness and have to go up a bra cup size. You'll definitely want to refresh your bra wardrobe and try new brands, styles, and sizes.

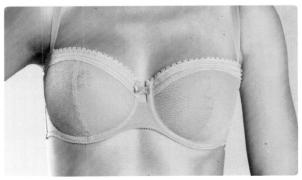

Chantelle Parisian Demi Bra

Many women with more shallow breast tissue find that demi-cups and balconette bras lift their breasts back to where they were pre-pregnancy. You might also try a bra with removable "cookies" or "cutlets" to replace volume.

POST-SURGERY

These bras are worn immediately after any kind of breast surgery, be it cosmetic augmentation, reduction, or reconstruction after mastectomy. They can be compression-type garments that hold stitches in place, or looser-fitting designs made of softer fabrics, with a place to hold post-surgical drains. You'll want to talk to your surgeon to learn more about what style she recommends. Most post-surgical bras have adjustable Velcro closures in front and on the shoulders, making it easy to get in and out of the garment. Some cosmetic surgeons ask patients to wear specific styles to help reduce scarring.

A post-surgical bra may be worn for a few weeks or a few months, depending on your medical situation. Women recovering from breast reductions, breast lifts, or breast augmentations will wear them a shorter time, while those undergoing breast reconstruction might need to use them longer.

POST-BREAST IMPLANTS

Breast implants, whether used in reconstruction or for cosmetic purposes, move in a different way than regular breast tissue. Many women with implants find that they no longer need as much support in a bra. Many also find that their breast tissue is less malleable and that heavily seamed or underwire bras are less comfortable. Length and placement of wire can also be an issue if there is scarring.

POST-MASTECTOMY

These bras fall into three categories: traditional pocketed non-wired bras that hold prosthetic breast forms, less structured bras made for reconstructed breasts (made from patient's tissue or with breast implants), and bras designed for women with no reconstruction (remaining bi-laterally or unilaterally flat).

Pocketed bras have been on the market for years, but many were originally sold in specialty stores as "medical supplies," along with breast forms or prosthesis. Breast forms also come in all shapes, sizes, and weights, and are categorized by a number, not a cup size. Not all breast forms feel or fit the same way in every bra. The challenge of finding a form and a bra to work with a customer's surgical site or post-treatment body means it's best to visit a post-mastectomy bra fit specialist.

While it might be possible for some people to wear a pocketed mastectomy bra even with breast reconstruction after mastectomy, it will depend on the surgical site and type of breast reconstruction. For example, silicone implants don't move the same way as breasts constructed from a patient's fat. However, a few retailers (like Nordstrom) will add "pockets" to your existing bras.

Mastectomy bras are the hardest to fit because each person's sensitivity, scar tissue, and treatment are unique. Those with breast implants or with no reconstruction may find bralettes or other soft cup bras easiest to wear.

Ana Ono Sandi Front Close Post Reconstruction Bra

Anita Fleur Underwire Mastectomy Pocketed Bra

POST-MENOPAUSAL

No one brand is designing specifically for this population, although a few have taken notice that women over fifty have unique bra-wearing needs. Breast tissue undergoes another transformation at this time (similar to puberty) as glandular tissue is replaced by fat. About 20% of all women find that their breasts get bigger during menopause. They may feel heavier, and the skin more pliable. Older women also tend to lose muscle tone in their back, leading to sloping shoulders and difficulty keeping straps up. And if that's not enough, hormonal spikes may mean breast pain for a few weeks or months. (It all sounds like a ton of fun, right?) Tender skin means it's time to look for extras like triple-wrapped underwire and smart construction.

TRANSGENDER WOMEN

Fit issues for transgender women will either involve the use of breast forms in pocketed or non-pocketed bras (see post-mastectomy bras), or the issues typically associated with breast implants (see Post-Breast Implants). There may also be physical and psychological adjustments similar to issues associated with puberty and menopause. The good news is that there are now many online forums and retailers dedicated to helping trans women. Please see Appendix C for more infomation.

MEN WHO WEAR BRAS

Men wear bras for various reasons. Many bra retailers welcome male customers who need help with professional fittings. But not all their fitting issues are the same.

Male Crossdressers

Fit issues may have to do with torso length, and wider or more muscular backs. Many plus-size bra brands (with lengthier bands) don't always start at smaller cup sizes, and choosing the correct size breast form for a specific bra style can also be tricky. Bra extenders and other accessories listed in Chapter 7 can help tailor fit.

Men with Gynecomastia (Male Breast Growth)

There are no specific bra brands catering to men with gynecomastia, although more and more men are seeking out such support. Men with breasts usually have wider shoulders and torsos, and may find plus-size bra brands are their best solution. They can also use bra band extenders to add length to a regular bra (see Chapter 7). Men with gynecomastia typically have breasts that are also less full on top. Those with less breast tissue may be frustrated by the lack of wide band, small cups bras currently on the market. Bras that offer less projection and more compression are also an option.

❋ ❋ ❋

Next, we'll take a look at a special fit situation so common it deserves (and gets) a chapter of its own—sports bras.

CHAPTER 9

Sports Bras

HERE'S THE DEAL with sports bras: everybody needs one.

Yet surveys show nearly 70% of women do not wear sports bras when exercising. Even worse, fuller busted gals often don't participate in sports or athletic activities because keeping larger breasts restrained is a real challenge.

It's not like sports bras are hard to find. They're sold online and in most department stores, at various sporting outlets and retailers, and are even available in nursing and post-mastectomy styles. So why aren't women willing to invest in this essential piece of athletic equipment?

For some, it may have to do with price. Just like a well-constructed regular bra, many high-quality sports bras can cost anywhere from $50 to $90. I know I need more than one for a complete athletic wardrobe, too. A couple of sports bras can quickly add up to the price of one pair of name-brand running shoes.

> The modern sports bra was invented in the late 1970s, and was made by sewing together two jock straps.

Then there's the issue of finding one that fits. Visit your local sporting goods store and you'll find lots of people ready and willing to help you discover the perfect pair of running shoes. But most aren't trained to help you find a sports bra for your size, shape, and activity level.

Which is too bad, because there are several good reasons to wear a sports bra when exercising. Yes, we already learned that there's no real proof you will destroy Cooper's ligaments without one. But studies have indicated that there are serious advantages to wearing them.

1. They reduce pain and improve performance.

A majority of runners surveyed found pain relief with sports bras. Studies show that the right bra takes pressure off supporting muscles, can add to a female athlete's breathing and lung capacity, and helps reduce injuries. In other words, wearing a well-fitting sports bra provides the same benefit as a great pair of running shoes. You go further, faster, and with fewer risks.

2. Your regular bra isn't built for action.

Scientists have studied the dynamics of women's breasts when exercising—in fact, there are two universities dedicated to breast movement research. These studies have shown that our breasts don't just bobble up and down, but move in more of a figure-8 pattern. A well-made sports bra contains and restrains your breasts in a unique way so that you can get more from your workout. Plus most sports bras are made of materials designed to keep you cool and dry while you exercise.

3. Normal bras fall apart under pressure.

Your Cooper's ligaments may hold up just fine, but your everyday bra will be traumatized by the stress you put it under when you wear it to yoga, out for a run, or to Pilates. Plus, the delicate materials used to create a regular bra may be exposed to heavy perspiration, which can break down the material's elasticity. Do you really want to age your pretty bras before their time? Don't. Do. It.

4. Sports bra fashions rock.

Today's sports bras are super comfy to wear and are made to look great under running gear and yoga

Panache Full-Busted Underwire Sports Bra

clothes. Even if you don't make it to the gym, you'll feel more energized and athletic just wearing one!

5. They come in all sizes.

Yes, the full bust sports bra market continues to expand. Brands like Enell, Panache, and Elomi (and others) are working overtime to give fuller-busted women gorgeous options. Petite sports bra brands like Handful are covering the other end of the cup size spectrum, too. You'll find fashionable seasonal colors available so you can refresh your sports bra wardrobe regularly.

Sports bras have been around for centuries. Ancient drawings show Roman women exercising while wearing bandeau-like styles to cover and hold their breasts.

So how do you find the right sports bra? Since there may not be someone available to help fit you in a store, test it out yourself in the dressing room by running in place or doing jumping jacks. Choose brands that indicate what level of impact—high, medium or low—each bra style is designed to accommodate. Or shop from a retailer, in-person or online, that provides direction, like Title IX or HerRoom, among others. (For more sports bra retailers, see Chapter 10.)

SPORTS BRA TERMINOLOGY

There are two main styles of sports bras: compression and encapsulation. Encapsulation bras keep your breasts separate, each in its own space—not unlike separate cups. Compression bras hold you in place without cups and create more of a smooshed, uni-boob look under athletic tops. Many encapsulation models have compression features to double the support and containment.

Elements of a Well-Fitting Sports Bra

You can evaluate best fit by starting with the six elements of good bra fit listed in Chapter 5. You should also look for these extras:

∗ Encapsulation plus compression design

∗ Snug band and padded straps

∗ Adjustable straps

∗ Convertible straps (to wear under T-back tanks)

∗ Moisture-wicking, anti-bacterial, breathable fabric

∗ Adjustable hooks for easier exit after a sweaty workout

∗ Pockets to hold padding or for extra nipple coverage

How many sports bras do you need? It all depends on your level of activity. Unlike regular bras, you'll need to wash yours after every workout. If you exercise more than twice a week, you'll want at least two or even three good sports bras for a complete bra wardrobe.

SAMPLING OF SPORTS BRA BRANDS
BY SIZE AND TYPE

(Sizes in US unless otherwise noted. Not all cups available in every band size.)

BRAND	BAND	CUPS	TYPE
Anita	30-46	A-H	
Anita Care	30-42	A-E	Post-Mastectomy
Berlei	30-44	B-J (UK)	
Cake Lingerie	32-40	B-K	Maternity
Chantelle	30-42	C-G	
Champion	32-46	A-DDD	
Elomi	34-46	D-J (UK)	
Enell	00-8 (fits approx 32C to 50DD)		
Freya	28-40	B-H (UK)	
Handful	32-40	AA-C	Removable Padding
Little Bra Company	28-38	A-C	
Lululemon	32-40	A-E	

BRAND	BAND	CUPS	TYPE
Moving Comfort	30-44	A-E	
Panache	28-40	B-J (UK)	
Shock Absorber	30-44	A-G (UK)	
Title IX	32-48	AA-F	
Victoria's Secret	30-40	AA-DD	

Now that you've gotten a complete rundown of the different bra styles available and what they do, you're ready to go bra shopping. That's what the next chapter is all about.

CHAPTER 10

Shopping for Every Body

WE'RE FINALLY at the shopping part of The Bra Zone experience. You're ready to try out a range of sizes and styles and build your ideal bra wardrobe. But where do you start? Do you head to the mall, find a local lingerie boutique, or start your search online? There's no reason why you can't explore all of these intimate apparel shopping opportunities.

You might find it easier to approach the task if you compare it to the way you shop for your shoes. Sometimes you buy expensive designer heels at a high-end store, other times you shop for bargain pairs at a discount store. Not many people buy all their footwear from the same place or always at the same price point.

There's a vast spectrum of quality in my shoe wardrobe, just as there is with my lingerie.

Where you are located will make a difference. Your city might be home to a dozen lingerie shops that carry a great selection of brands and sizes. You can quickly find customer reviews online to get an idea of their in-store experience, and even call ahead to make an appointment if you're not sure they carry your size.

I live in Los Angeles, a large sprawling metropolis where you'd think it would be simple to find multiple stores to meet any of my bra needs. But I still face a few challenges. I've aged and sized out of the Victoria's Secret mall boutiques, so those are not an option for me. There are plenty of luxury boutiques, but they don't carry styles and sizes that work for my boobs or body.

Through trial and error, I've narrowed down a couple of favorite places where the salespeople know my tastes and take great care of me. I still like to browse my local department stores, though, and enjoy shopping from boutique e-retailers. Plus, when I travel on business or for pleasure, I try to stop into stores I've discovered through lingerie blogs or social media.

Following lingerie bloggers is a good way to stay up to date on the latest brands and industry news. Esty Lingerie (unaffiliated with Etsy) has compiled a database of over 120 bloggers, grouped by area of expertise. Although they represent a mostly under-thirty age demographic, it is possible to match yourself up with someone who wears sizes that fit within your general Bra Zone. Reading product reviews from bloggers can save you loads of time and money. One of the largest and most comprehensive websites, the Lingerie Addict, also provides newsletter subscribers with a list of weekly lingerie sales from all over the world. (For more on lingerie blogs, see Appendix C.)

There are hundreds of brands available to bra shoppers, and more if you count independents and e-retailers. It's not possible to list every outlet in this book, but the following will give you a good start on your search. You'll find more stores and brands organized by sizes and fashion style offered in Appendix C.

Here are a few places to start your in-store and online bra shopping experience:

1. Intimate Apparel E-retailers

These websites are dedicated to selling intimate apparel, including swimwear, loungewear, sleepwear, maternity, men's underwear, and accessories. They generally offer a very wide range of brands, sizes, and styles (sports, maternity, and some post-mastectomy). Most make it super easy to search for your style and size and to review other customer comments. Fit specialists are available by phone or email to assist customers. Examples: Bare Necessities, HerRoom, Figleaves (UK), Freshpair.

Looking to buy—or sell—nearly new bras? There's an active secondary bra marketplace on websites like Ebay, Bratabase, and Reddit's /r/BraSwap.

2. Department Stores

Many department store lingerie sections maintain a good selection of everyday, sports, and maternity brands, both in-stores and online. They have a similar search and review system as the dedicated intimate apparel e-retailers above. Some offer onsite bra-fitting services, which are often sponsored by specific brands. Discount department stores (like Target) carry less-expensive versions of better intimate apparel lines. Some online-only department stores carry international brands that you might not find anywhere else (except direct from the manufacturer). Examples: Amazon, Bergdorf-Goodman, Nordstrom, Bloomingdales, Macy's, Target, Kohl's, Zulily.

3. Fashion and Clothing Retailers

These shops typically specialize by fashion style (contemporary to luxury) and customer demographic. They either create their own intimate apparel labels or offer brands that fit their fashion niche. Examples: Aerie for American Eagle, Anthropologie, ASOS (UK), Bravissimo (full cup and plus-size), Lane Bryant/Cacique (plus-size), Nasty Gal, Soma Intimates (over-thirty market).

4. Specialty Clothing Stores

There are numerous maternity, post-mastectomy, bridal, and athletic clothing stores that carry their own, and other brands. See specialty listings in Appendix C.

5. Lingerie Retailers

Big or small, retailers like Victoria's Secret are about their own brand. Their aim is to be your go-to lingerie destination for their specific fashion aesthetic, even if their store only exists online. Some, like AdoreMe, have a subscription service that sends you a new bra set every month. Examples: Addiction Lingerie, Agent Provocateur, Journelle, LaPerla, Negative Underwear, Rigby & Peller (UK & US), ThirdLove, Trashy Lingerie, True&Co., What Katie Did.

You'll find some companies selling lingerie through trained "stylists." Peach and Essential Bodywear send fitters to your home or office.

6. Independent Lingerie Boutiques

There are thousands of clothing and lingerie boutiques in the United States. That number is likely much larger if you count lingerie e-retailers. Many have more than one store, too (for instance, Jenette Bras has three locations in the Los Angeles area). They carry a selection of brands to meet their customer's needs, and a few carry their own labels. Lingerie boutiques distinguish themselves through individual customer service, so this is where you'll find retailers who are willing to set up "virtual" video or phone fittings with out-of-area customers. Examples: A Sophisticated Pair, Bluestockings Boutique, Contours Lingerie, Livi Rae Lingerie, the Bra Lounge, Secrets From Your Sister, Zovo Lingerie.

7. Brand Websites
These can be major players found in department stores or exclusive lingerie boutiques, or they can be small shops making everything by hand. Some, like Claudette, offer discounts on older season's stock on their websites. Examples: Between the Sheets, Cosabella, Hanky Panky, Harlow & Fox, Kiss Me Deadly, Tia Lyn, Trashy Lingerie, What Katie Did.

8. Online Marketplaces
You can find something completely unique and hand-made from independent designers through these websites. Many sellers are willing to customize lingerie orders, if asked. Examples: Amazon, ASOS, Etsy, and Ebay.

9. "Virtual" Lingerie Stores
These are e-boutiques or blogs that curate a selection of bra styles, but don't carry any physical inventory. Many fashion blogs receive a small percentage of direct sales when readers buy products through affiliate partners (this is one way of paying for the overhead costs of running a website). At the Breast Life Store

(www.thebreastlife.com/store) I've compiled a selection of highly rated brands and accessories in various style categories. If you decide to make a purchase, you are sent to a retailer's website to complete a sale. Some of the links, but not all, are tied to affiliate partners.

✻   ✻   ✻

You may have noticed that many of the names listed above could fall into one or more categories. Some brands have one storefront and a huge online presence, or their lines are available through other channels and boutiques. Some might extend discounts to consumers via their website. The old-fashioned business model of a manufacturer selling to a retailer who then in turn sells to a customer is more flexible and fluid in today's intimate apparel marketplace.

DOS AND DON'TS OF BUYING LINGERIE ONLINE

↝ **DO** visit a few different sites to discover which ones suit you best.

You may be more comfortable shopping from big online retailers like HerRoom or Bare Necessities. But you should check out smaller retailers that may better fit your fashion aesthetic and budget. There are also websites that specialize, like Hips & Curves (plus sizes), Lula Lu Petites (small busts), and Dollhouse Bettie (vintage inspired), to name just a few.

If you're looking for something handmade or more unique, you can shop Etsy.com or smaller e-boutiques. There are tons of places to buy lingerie online, including direct from brands. Check out the list in Appendix C for more ideas.

🖝 DO carefully read website return policies before you order.

You may be asked to return items a certain way (to avoid crushing a molded-cup bra, for example). Read the fine print before you place your order, and never rip off price tags until you're absolutely sure you're satisfied with your purchase.

🖝 DO begin by ordering bra styles or lingerie brands that you already prefer. Not every bra style fits every woman. Think about the bras you've worn to shreds. Did they offer minimum or maximum coverage? Were they padded, have contour, or softer seam or lace cups? Narrow down the style of bra or brands you prefer, even before size.

🖝 DO read customer reviews. Not sure about a bra? Most websites include customer feedback. Many offer info not only on bra size, but height, age, and even body shape of bra raters. Spend a little time finding out whether the bra fits true to size before you order.

🖝 DO order some matching panties to go with your new purchase. Seasonal fashion colors often sell out, so it's best to buy at the same time. (You may also be able to find less expensive complimentary knickers in other brands.)

⌒ DON'T be overwhelmed by all the choices. All the styles and brands may feel intimidating at first. Use the lingerie website's search engine to narrow down selections in your size, style, and brand preferences.

⌒ DON'T forget to include international customs or shipping fees when considering price. Some international retailers waive fees on post-mastectomy bras.

⌒ DON'T expect to wear the same size across all bra brands and styles. Most sites offer additional advice, and you can open up specific brand sizing windows with useful, added info. Retailers are usually happy to answer questions via phone or email.

⌒ DON'T be disappointed if the bra arrives, fits well, but you don't like the way it looks or feels on your body or under your clothes. Technical fit is only one aspect of finding a great bra. Remember that if one bra isn't right, another will be.

You may want to make an appointment or be asked by a salesperson at a store whether you'd like a fitting. What should you expect?

Tiny boutiques or big department stores can go through the same fit motions or be drastically different. Most fit specialists (in the United States) are female.

An exceptional bra fitter can glance at a customer and nail their exact size. Others use a measuring tape and wrap it around your ribs, bust, or upper bust to help calculate size. One method is not better than another.

Bra measurements are taken while you are wearing your bra, or sometimes you are asked to put on a special "fitting" bra. Fitters usually want to see how your current bra looks on you because it gives them information on your preferences—or in what way it no longer provides shape and support. Once they've settled on a few sizes (yes, they are well aware of The Bra Zone), they'll bring you half a dozen to try on. It's only by putting on these different brands and styles (not unlike jeans, shoes, or swimwear) that you'll find something you're excited to purchase.

What are the qualities of a "good" bra fitter? According to fit expert Ali Cudby, it is a person who asks questions about your personal preferences and listens to you. It also helps if you have a good idea of how you like a bra to fit on your body, know what you're willing to spend, and have realistic expectations. A good bra fitter will search through their store's inventory to find exactly what you need.

If you have any concerns about how an in-store fitting is carried out, check online customer reviews of stores or call ahead and ask questions. No one should ever make you feel uncomfortable or awkward in a dressing room. If a salesperson doesn't treat you with respect, take your business elsewhere.

Buying direct from manufacturers or retailers (online or in a store) is your way of voting with your wallet for the brands, sizes, and styles you want retailers to carry. If they don't know they have a customer for a product, they aren't about to order it from a manufacturer. But bras aren't the only items you may want to buy from these outlets. You'll also want to invest in products to help extend the life of your new lingerie investments. The next chapter will give you pointers on how to care for and store your bras.

CHAPTER 11

Bra Wardrobe Wear, Care, and Storage

HOW MANY TIMES you have to replace your bra wardrobe depends a lot on how often you wear, and how you care for, your intimate apparel. A general guideline is to treat your lingerie the way you'd want a partner to handle your breasts: with thoughtfulness and a gentle touch. You might think this applies only to the chore of laundering delicate items. But how you put on your bra (covered in Chapter 5), how long you wear it, and how it is stored can also extend its life and your investment.

So let's get down to the big question: how often should you wash your bras? The answer is "it all depends." You'll wash an everyday bra more often than

TBZ TIP Use a fabric pen to mark a bra's label with the month and year purchased. That way you have a reality check on when to replace it.

you will one that is worn occasionally, like perhaps a strapless style. It also depends on how much you perspire, where you live, and what you've been doing while wearing your bra. For example, you'll want to throw a sweat-soaked sports bra in the wash after a long run.

Most intimate apparel brands recommend that you let a bra "rest" between wears to allow the fabric to return to its former (not-so-stretched-out) shape. What this means is that it's best to wear a bra for a day, or maybe two consecutive days, and switch to a different one. You may or may not need to wash it after those two days, depending on how much sweat you feel you left on the garment, but remember that body oils break down the delicate fabrics in a bra.

I recommend rotating through two or three bras every week, and then washing them all on laundry day.

As I mentioned earlier, the average woman owns nine bras but only wears six of them on a regular basis. Your bra wardrobe might consist of three or four everyday bras, in various styles, plus a few sports bras, and then a strapless, multi-way, or front close bra you wear on special occasions or in the summer months. You may also wear a sleep bra or choose to wear a larger cup size during hormonal times of the month (similar to owning a few "period panties"). This way, when you have a few in the wash, you'll always have a couple that are ready to wear.

FOUR BRA WEAR AND CARE RULES

1. Adjust.

When was the last time you adjusted the length of your bra straps? How about the band? Take time to readjust straps and bands on occasion to get the most wear from your foundations. Be gentle when putting on and taking off.

2. Rotate.

Switch up your bras every couple of days, trying to even out wear and tear on them. An easy way to keep track of how many times you've worn one bra is to keep a few pair of matching panties stored nearby, or even inside their cups. Once you are out of assigned knickers, you know it's time to launder that bra.

3. Organize.

With today's greater variety of bra styles, not all bras fit neatly into the same old storage space. I own dozens in different shapes and sizes, from strapless, long-line, demi-cups, and molded to sports bras. Molded or T-shirt bras should be stored in a way that won't crush the cups (stacked or hung). Cut and sewn bras can be folded. Keep hooks clasped so that they don't snag fabric. Use shoe or gift boxes in your drawers to keep bras and panties organized. I also keep a mesh laundry bag nearby to hold my soiled bras so they aren't accidentally laundered with the rest of my dirty clothing.

4. Wash by hand and hang dry.

I can see you wincing at this rule, and believe me I feel your pain. I used to hate the thought of hand washing my delicates. But fabric care has evolved and hand washing can actually be much easier than running a load of delicates. There are no-rinse soaps (like Soak and Eucalan) that make hand laundering a ten-minute chore with amazing results. If you must wash your bras in a washing machine, remember to put them in a mesh laundry bag, fasten all hooks, and use a cool water temperature and very mild detergent.

ANSWERS TO COMMON BRA WASH AND WEAR QUESTIONS

1. How often should you wash your bra?

You don't need to launder your delicates after every wear unless you've been in a heat wave or a sweaty workout at the gym or yoga studio. Not washing your bra enough and washing your bras too often both break down the delicate elastic, lace, and foam materials. It's a personal decision, and your best bet is to create a system that helps you keep track of how many times you've worn a particular bra.

Best way to extend your bra investment? Keep them out of the dryer!! High heat destroys delicate foam and fabric. Always hang to dry after washing.

2. How often should you replace a bra?

You know that feeling when you get a new bra that fits great and makes you feel fabulous? How about the way you feel when you put on a worn out brassiere? If you look in the mirror and don't like the way your boobs look, your bra probably isn't working for you anymore. Even if your boobs haven't changed size or shape, fabrics will wear, bands stretch out, and straps collapse. If you don't feel good about it, it's time to toss out the old and bring in some new support.

3. How long should a bra last?

Industry experts disagree on longevity because not all bras are created equally. Some may only last six months to a year, even less if they aren't laundered by hand or are tossed in the dryer (that's the primary reason some wires pop out of casements). A well-made bra worn on a regular basis should last a year or longer. But if you don't wear it often, you can keep a bra for several years—as long as it still fits. Strapless bras fall into this category for me. My size tends to change before I've worn one out.

FOUR BRA STORAGE TIPS TO EXTEND THE LIFE OF YOUR LINGERIE

1. Secure. Hook up any loose hardware to avoid damaging fine fabrics.

2. Separate. Divide up your bras from most to least used so you can find what you need for everyday wear.

3. Sort. Lacy and soft cup bras can be folded in half, with straps tucked inside. T-shirt, molded, and padded cups must be "stacked" or hung. Otherwise, dents and bends will damage them.

4. Scent. Tie a few sachets to hangers, or stash some yummy smelling soap in your lingerie drawer. Lavender sachets double as natural moth repellants.

BRA RECYCLING RESOURCES

Manufactured textiles (including common synthetics found in bras, such as polyester, spandex, and nylon) may take from twenty to 200 years to completely break down. That's a big difference from the natural fibers found in a cotton T-shirt, which only takes six months to decompose. If you're like most consumers, you toss out your old bras—which means tons of used bras may be around for decades, if not centuries.

As a more eco-friendly alternative, here are nine places to recycle well-worn or gently used bras. These for-profit and non-profit resources will put your bras to good use and keep them out of landfills.

1. The Bra Recyclers This company distributes gently used and new bras to over eighty organizations serving the homeless and domestic violence victims all over the world. The easy-to-use locator on their website shows you the nearest drop-off location (they are also now partnering with Soma stores in the US). You can mail them your clean bras, or hold your own bra collection event.

2. Bra Recycling Agency They take old, worn-out bras, pulverize them, and turn them into special-event carpeting. Funds received from selling bra metal and wires are given to breast cancer research.

3. Breast Oasis A non-profit providing needy women with clean, gently-used bras. They have multiple donation locations in the US, or you can pay a small fee via PayPal to ship them.

4. Free the Girls Non-profit working with safe houses that help survivors of human trafficking make a living by selling used clothing. There are multiple drop-offs for your gently-used bras throughout the US and Canada. They also accept bra donations by mail, asking a "buck a bra" to cover shipping costs.

5. Goodwill Industries Clean, gently-used bras are sold in their stores and benefit work training programs. Bras that can no longer be worn are sold for scrap but still benefit this non-profit.

6. Oxfam This UK-based non-profit sells gently-used bras in one of its 700 stores and recycles old bras at their recycling facility.

7. Soma This bra retailer holds an annual bra drive (#OneMillionBras) to benefit the National Network to End Domestic Violence. Simply bring a gently-used bra to any Soma store during the campaign.

8. Uplift Bras This charitable organization collects new and second-hand bras and distributes them to needy communities. Based out of Australia and New Zealand, they supply bras to women in third-world countries.

9. USAgain Another for-profit textile recycling company that has donation bins located all over the US, and takes any and all clean and dry clothing. They wholesale used clothing to second hand shops throughout the world.

❊ ❊ ❊

Keep these cleaning, storage, and recycling tips in mind, and your bras will enjoy a full and productive life, both in your lingerie drawer—and beyond. Read on for the Ten Bra Rules that will ensure your bra experience is the best it can be.

CHAPTER 12

Ten Rules for Bra Zone Bliss

CONGRATULATIONS! You now know the sizes that fit into your personal Bra Zone, a good idea of where to find them, and the best way to care for your intimates. You've also discovered the styles you prefer and which bra brands to look for the next time you want or need to buy one. You should have a few blogger and retail brand resources bookmarked to consult in between any future lingerie shopping expeditions. You might even be inspired to take stock of your lingerie drawers and do a complete overhaul of your foundation needs. If so, I've done my job. You should feel less intimidated by the whole bra buying and fitting process.

But before you put this book on the shelf (or loan it to a bosom buddy), pay close attention to this final chapter. It may be the most important one in this book.

It serves as a reminder that it's going to take some time to change your mindset about how you approach the business of buying bras. That old "85% of women wear the wrong bra size" myth is still stuck in all our heads (including mine). It's repeated in nearly every bra news and fashion story, and is a mantra of many bra fitters. Every time I read or hear this "fact," I cringe. Why? It serves as a negative and unproductive message to consumers. First we are told that we can't trust our own judgment when it comes to fit and size; and then that we should leave matters of bra buying to professionals because it is all too complicated for us to understand.

The purpose of this book is to help shoppers see that bra shopping does not have to be a painful chore. It can be fun, easy, and empowering.

TEN RULES TO HELP YOU FIND AND STAY IN YOUR BRA ZONE

1. Appreciate your originality.

Yes, your breasts are constantly changing and may be a burden at times (for whatever reason). But they are also unique, wondrous, and yours alone. Check out the "Know Your Breasts" section on HerRoom.com, scroll through the photo galleries at 007b.com or Bratabase, and get to know better the wide variety of breast shapes and sizes found in nature. No two boobs are alike, even on the same woman. Accept your originality and don't blame your breasts if a particular bra doesn't fit.

2. Be curious.

Discover the joys of different styles and brands. Find a blogger with your body type or boob shape and look for recommendations. Shop for new lingerie seasonally, like you often do with clothing or shoes. That way you'll always have the correct foundations to wear under the latest fashions. Don't be disheartened if you have to change sizes and styles; just remember that there's always something new you can try.

3. Don't let others label you.

You now know that no two brands or styles will fit you the same way. Be open to new band/cup combinations. The only constant is that your boobs (and taste) are sure to change. Keep in mind the different fitting formulas and international size tables. Focus less on an arbitrary letter and number and more on what makes you feel and look your best.

4. Remember your sisters.

If you aren't dead set on being one distinct size, it will be easier to turn to sister sizing to get the best fit. Moving up and down bra bands is easy if you remember the formula. If you go up a band size, you need to go down a cup size to maintain your same cup volume and vice versa.

5. Invest in yourself.

Even if you can't buy high-quality pieces every time you shop, you can focus on putting together a total lingerie "outfit" by purchasing multiple matching panties. You'll feel more in charge and together when you're rocking a coordinated ensemble underneath it all.

6. Keep learning.

It's not just your boobs that will continue to change and evolve. New brands and materials make a difference in bra size and fit. Racer-back, sports, demi-cup, plunge, lace, and T-shirt molded bras offer distinct breast profiles. Don't be confused by the options. Instead, research the possibilities!

7. Let go of the past.

Rotate, replenish, and re-adjust your bras. Don't wear the same bra each and every day. Don't hold on to tired old bras since they'll just make you feel bad. Set aside some time to visit your favorite store or look for replacements online.

8. Take time out for self-care.

Don't throw your bra in a drawer—or on the floor—after a long day. Keep your lingerie organized so you can find what you need and extend the life of your purchases. Can't bring yourself to hand-wash your bras? Invest in a lingerie laundry bag, use gentle soap, cool water, and the delicate cycle of the washing machine. Always air dry. Never, ever, ever put your bras in the dryer.

9. Don't compare yourself to anyone else.

Everyone has a unique size, shape, or breast experience. Surveys show that women wear anywhere from six to eight different sizes of bras in their lifetime. (I wore that many in one pregnancy!) Know that being human means facing these ups and downs, whether from weight changes, pregnancy, or age. Don't let normal bra challenges defeat you. And that friend with the fabulous rack and perfect body? Believe me, she has her own issues.

10. You are worthy.

Bra fit and size are only a small part of the bra wear experience. Lifestyle, income, age, and body size are also important considerations. You'll have days when nothing seems to work for you. Sometimes you'll need to customize your bra to get the best fit under certain outfits or circumstances. Show a little compassion to yourself and remember that your Bra Zone is a lot like you: growing, changing, and getting wiser with time.

Acknowledgments

The idea for *The Bra Zone* began as an "aha!" moment at a writing retreat in Taos, New Mexico. During conversations with fellow bra wearers, I suddenly realized that despite years of bra wearing, no one felt confident about their own bra shopping skills. Everyone knew what they liked, but no one seemed to know quite how to find it. An outline of the book sat on my computer for far too long. It wasn't until a full year had gone by that I found the time to finish a completed draft. One thing I learned along the way: plug away at anything for long enough and eventually it will get done.

You would not be holding *The Bra Zone* in your hand (or reading it on your tablet) without the book publishing smarts of Janica Smith of PublishingSmith, (janicasmith.com/publishingsmith). Her encouragement throughout delays and setbacks was invaluable, as were her connections to a supportive group of professionals needed to make the book a reality. I'm grateful for the extraordinary talents of designer Laura Shaw of Laura Shaw Design (lshawdesign.com), and illustrator Allison Meierding (allisonmeierding.com).

Thanks also to my patient editor, Lisa Canfield of Copy Coach Lisa (www.copycoachlisa.com), for her sense of humor as I kept missing deadlines.

What you'll find in these pages is the product of my many years attending lingerie trade shows, researching and writing for intimate-apparel outlets, following numerous lingerie bloggers, and listening to others who make a living working in the industry. Here, in alphabetical order, are those who patiently answered my questions or provided information through their informative articles:

* Erica Windle, A Sophisticated Pair

* Jeanna Kadlec, Bluestockings Boutique

* Moira Nelson, Bra La Mode

* Claire Dumican, Butterfly Collection

* Frederika Zappe, Eveden Inc.

* Ali Cudby, Fab Foundations

* Holly Jackson, The Full Figured Chest

* Cora Harrington, The Lingerie Addict

* Ellen Lewis, Lingerie Briefs

* Luis Paredes, The Lingerie Journal

* Jenette Goldstein, Jenette Bras

- Sweets, Sweet Nothings

- Victoria Roberts, Zovo Lingerie

I'd also like to thank the brands that generously provided images of their products. Last, but not least, a round of applause to my friends and colleagues who took the time to read an early draft of the book: Alison Connolly, Heidi Eriksen, Betsy Farber, and Leah Patterson. Their helpful comments and suggestions were much appreciated.

Appendix A

SISTER SIZE CUP VOLUME CHART (US SIZES)

Sister Sizes or Equivalent Cup Volumes Across Bra Bands

Band	28	30	32	34	36	38
	28B	30A				
	28C	30B	32A			
	28D	30C	32B	34A		
	28E	30D	32C	34B	36A	
	28F	30E	32D	34C	36B	38A
	28G	30F	32E	34D	36C	38B
	28H	30G	32F	34E	36D	38C
	28I	30H	32G	34F	36E	38D
	28J	30I	32H	34G	36F	38E
	28K	30J	32I	34H	36G	38F
		30K	32J	34I	36H	38G
			32K	34J	36I	38H
				34K	36J	38I
					36K	38J
						38K

40	42	44	46	48	50	52
40A						
40B	42A					
40C	42B	44A				
40D	42C	44B	46A			
40E	42D	44C	46B	48A		
40F	42E	44D	46C	48B	50A	
40G	42F	44E	46D	48C	50B	52A
40H	42G	44F	46E	48D	50C	52B
40I	42H	44G	46F	48E	50D	52C
40J	42I	44H	46G	48F	50E	52D
40K	42J	44I	46H	48G	50F	52E
	42K	44J	46I	48H	50G	52F
		44K	46J	48I	50H	52G
			46K	48J	50I	52H
				48K	50J	52I
					50K	52J
						52K

Appendix B

INTERNATIONAL BRA SIZE CHARTS

The following is compiled from several lingerie guides. Please check with individual brands for actual values used in your country.

INTERNATIONAL BRA CUP SIZE CONVERSION

US	UK	EU	Japan	France	Australia/NZ
AAA	AAA				
AA	AA	AA	A		
A	A	A	B	A	A
B	B	B	C	B	B
C	C	C	D	C	C
D	D	D	E	D	D
DD/E	DD	E	F	E	DD
DDD/F	E	F	G	F	E
DDDD/G	F	G	H	G	F
DDDDD/H	FF	H	I	H	FF
DDDDDD/I	G	I	J	I	G
J	GG	J	K	J	GG
K	H	K	l	K	H
L	HH	L	M	L	HH
M	J	M	N	M	J
N	JJ	N	O	N	JJ
O	K	O	P		K
	L				

INTERNATIONAL BRA BAND SIZE CONVERSION

US	UK	EU/Japan	France	Australia/NZ
28	28	60	75	6
30	30	65	80	8
32	32	70	85	10
34	34	75	90	12
36	36	80	95	14
38	38	85	100	16
40	40	90	105	18
42	42	95	110	20
44	44	100	115	22
46	46	105	120	24
48	48	110	125	26
50	50	115	130	28
52	52	120	135	30

Appendix C

BRA AND BLOGGER RESOURCES

The following selection of bra brands, retailers, and bloggers represents different budgets, fashion styles, and bra fit situations. For even more recommendations, please visit TheBreastLife.com.

General Bra and Lingerie Industry Resources

Amazon
BareNecessities
Bratabase (Bra Sizing & Listings)
Esty Lingerie (Blogger Database)
Fab Foundations (Bra Fit Training)
Figleaves
HerRoom
Hurray Kimmay* (Personal Bra Shopping Service)
Lingerie Talk*
Lingerie Briefs*
McPete Sez*
Nordstrom
The Lingerie Addict* (Weekly Sales Roundup)
The Lingerie Journal*
Reddit/ABraThatFits Community (Retailer Listings)

Bra Reviews

A Sophisticated Pair
Comics Girls Need Bras*
Curvy Wordy*
H Cup Chronicles*
Invest in Your Chest*
Sweet Nothings*
The Daily Knicker*
The Lingerie Addict*
Two Cakes on a Plate*
(More blogger bra reviews listed under each category, below.)

Bra Care & Accessories

Braza
Commando
Eucalan Delicate Wash
Fashion Forms
Forever New
Nippies by Bristols 6
Rixie Clip
Soak Wash
Strap Saver
The Brag Company

KEY: *Active Bloggers; **Inactive Bloggers

Special Fit Situations

Young Girls & Teens

Aerie

Angel First
  (Marks & Spencer)

Avia

Boobs & Bloomers

Champion

Jockey Girls

Maidenform

Royce

Tucker + Tate

Tween Bee

Yellowberry

*(See also Petite & Small
Bust below.)*

Full Bust (DD+)
& Full Figure

Addition Elle

AdoreMe (Membership
  Website)

An Enhanced Experience*

Avocado Lingerie

A Sophisticated Pair

A Tale of Two Boobs*

Becky's Boudoir*

Big Cup, Little Cup*

Bosom Galore

Bras and Body Image*

Brastop

Brava Lingerie

Bravissimo

Broad Lingerie

Butterfly Collection**

Buttress & Snatch

Claudette

Contours Lingerie

Comexim

Comics Girls Need Bras*

Curvy Kate

Curvy Couture

Curvy Wordy*

Elila

Elomi

Empreinte

Ewa-Michalak

Fantasie

Figleaves

Full Beauty

Fuller Figure Fuller Bust*

Freya

Goddess

Gossard

H Cup Chronicles*

Harlow & Fox

Hips & Curves

Invest In Your Chest*

Jenette Bras

Lane Bryant (Cacique
  Intimates)

Leading Lady

Lingerie Detective*

Miss Mandalay

Panache

Parfait by Affinitas

Playful Promises

Playtex

PrimaDonna/Twist

Samanta

Scarlet's Letter*

South Bay Boobology

Sweet Nothings*

The Full Figured Chest*

The Petite Collegiate*

Tia Lyn Lingerie
Two Cakes on a Plate*
Tutti Rouge
Thin & Curvy*
Urban Intimates
Zulily (Membership
  Webstie)

LGBTQIA+ Friendly
A Sophisticated Pair
Bluestockings Boutique
Bravissimo (Transgender
  Bra Fittings)
Broad Lingerie
Chrysalis Lingerie
Danaë
Dottie's Delights
Flattopper Pride
FYI by Dani Read
Origami Customs
Play Out Underwear
Rebirth Garments
Secrets From Your Sister
The Breast Life
The Lingerie Addict*
The Lingerie Lesbian**
Tomboy Exchange

Maternity & Nursing
A Mother's Boutique
Anita
Belabumbum
Bella Materna
Bravado
Cache Coeur Lingerie
Cake Maternity
Carriwell
Dairy Fairy

Destination Maternity/
  Motherhood Maternity/
  A Pea in the Pod
Emma-Jane
Figure 8 Maternity
Ingrid & Isabel
Lorna Drew
Hotmilk
La Leche League
  International
Majamas
PumpEase
Rosie Pope
Royce
Seraphine Maternity
Simple Wishes
The Pump Station
Village Maternity
You! Lingerie
*(Other brands making
nursing bra styles:
Cosabella, Elila, Elomi,
Freya, Goddess, Heidi
Klum, Leonisa, Leading
Lady, Le Mystere, Marie Jo,
Mimi Holliday, Panache,
Playtex, and QT Intimates.
Nursing bras can also
be found at department
stores and online retailer
websites.)*

Petite & Small Bust
(AAA-B)
Anteocularis*
Cosabella
Eberjey

Hanky Panky
Honeydew
Itty Bitty Bra
Kurvendiskussionen
   (Austria)*
Little Women
Lost in Lingerie*
Lula Lu Petite Lingerie
Morning Madonna*
Of Lambs And Lace*
Relique
The Little Bra Company
Timpa
Wacoal/b.tempt'd
Write Me Bad Checks*
Ysé Lingerie

Post-Surgical &
Post-Mastectomy
American Breast Care
   (ABC)
Amoena
AnaOno Intimates
Anita Care
BFFL Co.
Bras Without Wires
By Baby's Rules**
Classique
Coobie
Coeur de Lys
Flattopper Pride
Heart & Core
Jamu Australia
Jodee (JC Penney)
Lorna Drew
Linda the Bra Lady
LuisaLuisa
Millie

Nearly Me
Nicola Jane
Nordstrom (sew-in-pocket
   service and specially
   trained fitters)
Red Fern Lingerie
Royce
Science & Silicone**
Soma Intimates
Sophia Rose
TLC (affiliate of American
   Cancer Society)
The Pink Bra

Sports Bras &
Active-Wear Bras
Adidas
Athleta
Avocado Sportswear
Big 5
Brooks/Moving Comfort
Dick's Sporting Goods
Heroine Sport
Koral Activewear
Kohl's
Lady Foot Locker
Lucy Activewear
Lululemon Athletica
Nike
Outdoor Voices
REI
SheFit
Sweaty Betty
Title Nine
*(Additional brands by size
listed in Chapter 9. Sports
bras can also be found at
department stores and
online retailer websites.)*

Men Who Wear Bras
A Sophisticated Pair
Butterfly Collection**
Crossdressers.com
Gynecomastia.org
HerRoom
  (lingerie-for-men)
Lisagirl.net*
Männerbusensupport*
  (Germany)
My Weekend Shoes*
Secrets From Your Sister
Sexy Crossdresser Gurl*
The Bra Guy*

BRA BRANDS & RETAILERS BY STYLE

Note: Many companies fall under more than one style category (e.g. basics, boudoir, and bridal).

Eco-Friendly & Sustainable
Araks
Between the Sheets
Bluestockings Boutique
Brook There
Clare Bare
Hanna Broer Design
harMonica
Nico Underwear
PACT
Skin
Underprotection
Under the Root

Basics
Aerie
Anthropologie
ASOS
Aubade
BareNecessities
Bravissimo
Calvin Klein
Chantelle
Claudette
Coobie
Cosabella
Eberjey
Elila
Elomi
Empreinte
Fantasie
Figleaves
Fleur't Intimates
Fortnight Lingerie
Freya
Hanky Panky
Hanro
HerRoom
Huit
Jenette Bras
Linda the Bra Lady
Lily of France
Livi Rae Lingerie
Macy's
Maidenform
Marie Jo
Naja
Nasty Gal
Negative Underwear
Nordstrom
Nubian Skin (Nude lingerie
  for WOC)

On Gossamer
Only Hearts
Panache
Peach (in-home fittings)
PrimaDonna/Twist
Rigby & Peller
Simone Perele
Soma Intimates
Target
ThirdLove (½ cup sizing)
Teddies for Bettys
TopShop
Town Shop NYC
Triumph
True&Co.
Vanity Fair
Victoria's Secret/PINK
Wacoal/b.tempt'd
Zovo Lingerie
Zulily (Membership
  website)

Luxury & Bridal

Absolutely Lingerie
Barneys
Bergdorf Goodman
Cadolle
Carine Gilson
Celeste
Chantal Thomass
Fleur of England
Fox & Rose
Gilda & Pearl
Glamuse
Harlow & Fox
Jane's Vanity
Journelle
Karolina Laskowska

La Perla
Layneau
Lille Boutique
Lise Charmel
Maison Lejaby
Marlies Dekkers
Nancy Meyer
Naked Princess
Net-a-Porter
OuiHours
The Giving Bride
VaBien
Violet's Knickers

Boudoir & Seduction

AdoreMe (Membership
  Website)
Agent Provocateur
Baci Lingerie
Bluebella
Bordelle
Fantasy Lingerie
Frederick's of Hollywood
Hips & Curves
KissKill
Lascivious
L'Agent
Oh La La Cheri
Playful Promises
Pleasurements
Seven 'til Midnight
Shirley of Hollywood
The Little Flirt (La Petite
  Coquette)
Tia Lyn Lingerie
Trashy Lingerie
Victoria's Secret
Yandy

Vintage Inspired

Angela Friedman
Buttress & Snatch
Dita Von Teese
Dollhouse Bettie
Dirty Dolls Lingerie
Dollydripp
Dottie's Delights
Etsy
Kiss Me Deadly

Lucy B (Lucy's Boudoir)
ModCloth
My Retro Closet
PinUp Girl Clothing
Rago
Secrets In Lace
Tutti Rouge
Trashy Diva
What Katie Did

Thanks for buying *The Bra Zone*. Please visit
TheBreastLife.com/TheBraZone to find more
brands, bloggers, and bra-buying resources. Just
enter the code "cupcake" to access bonus pages.